W9-AKT-678

Human Anatomy & Physiology I & II

With Questions & Answers Workbook and CD

Third Edition

Professor Jeffrey Hochbaum

Biology Department
Middlesex County College

THOMSON
™

Australia · Canada · Mexico · Singapore · Spain · United Kingdom · United States

THOMSON

Human Anatomy and Physiology I & II Laboratory

Professor Jeffrey Hochbaum

Executive Editor:
Michael Stranz

Managing Lab Editor:
Jeff Nunn

Custom Lab Editors:
Jeff Davies, John Horvath

Custom Production Editor:
Jennifer Flinchpaugh

Project Coordinators:
Lisa Donahue, Peg Hagar

Senior Pre-Press Specialist:
Riley Gibb

Cover Image:

www.ablestock.com

Production Supervisor-Labs:
Melanie Evans

Rights and Permissions Specialist:
Kalina Ingham Hintz

Senior Marketing Coordinator:
Sara Mercurio

The Adaptable Courseware Program may
consist of products and/or additions to
existing Thomson products that are
produced from camera-ready copy. Peer
review, class testing, and accuracy are
primarily the responsibility of the
author(s).

ISBN 978-1-426-63020-0
(1-426-63020-4)

International Divisions List

Asia (Including India):
Thomson Learning
(a division of Thomson Asia Pte Ltd)
5 Shenton Way #01-01
UIC Building
Singapore 068808
Tel: (65) 6410-1200
Fax: (65) 6410-1208

Australia/New Zealand:
Thomson Learning Australia
Level 7, 80 Dorcas Street
South Melbourne, Victoria 3205
Australia

Latin America:
Thomson Learning
Seneca 53
Colonia Polano
11560 Mexico, D.F., Mexico
Tel (525) 281-2906
Fax (525) 281-2656

Canada:
Thomson Nelson
1120 Birchmount Road
Toronto, Ontario
Canada M1K 5G4
Tel (416) 752-9100
Fax (416) 752-8102

UK/Europe/Middle East/Africa:
Thomson Learning
High Holborn House
50-51 Bedford Row
London, WC1R 4L$
United Kingdom
Tel 44 (020) 7067-2500
Fax 44 (020) 7067-2600

Spain (Includes Portugal):
Thomson Paraninfo
Calle Magallanes 25
28015 Madrid
España
Tel 34 (0)91 446-3350
Fax 34 (0)91 445-6218

To Joanie, Bandi, Coco and Puffy

PREFACE

Welcome to the exciting and fun-filled world of Human Anatomy & Physiology. Some of you may be wondering, what does he mean, exciting and fun-filled? The laboratory portion of the course is required, that's why I'm here!

Give me a moment to explain why I believe what is awaiting you during the laboratory portion of this course will be an exciting and fun-filled experience. You will be learning all about your body. What can be more exciting then learning and seeing what we are built of and how we are put together? To me, that can be very exciting.

For over 30 years of teaching I have had students tell me that if they had more time to review the material they are looking at in the laboratory portion of the course, they could easily get and "A" or at worst a "B" on the laboratory practical. However, community college students, like you, have a different life style then students attending four-year colleges. You may work and have a family to take care of. So it is very hard to return to campus and review the laboratory material, and we do not want students to dig up bodies to review body parts at home when their family is asleep

The hardest part of learning the material covered in the laboratory portion of the course is finding time to review all the histology, dissections, and models that you looked at during the laboratory class. Students are always asking "when can I come in and review the stuff I saw during the lab."

☆ *The purpose of this <u>Anatomy CD-ROM</u> and <u>Question and Answer (Q&A) Book</u> is to provide you with the opportunity and time to review the material you studied in the laboratory and test your knowledge whenever you want.*

☆ *By using the <u>Anatomy CD-ROM</u> and accompanying <u>Question and Answer (Q&A) Book</u> you can review and test yourself 24/7 (any time you want, when you are free) anywhere you have a computer.*

☆ *Print out the high-resolution anatomical images and carry them around in a binder to review 24/7. Use them as Giant Flash Cards.*

☆ *The <u>Anatomy CD-ROM</u> contains over 720 images of plastic anatomical models, organ dissections and histology that you will be studying during the laboratory portion of the course.*

Review, Review and More Review is the key to Success.

ACKNOWLEDGMENTS

Many people helped make *Human Anatomy & Physiology Laboratory Images for Student Review* possible. I would like to thank my best friend and wife, Joanie, for all her support and help and also Brian Richards and Barbara Bogner for their assistance and helpful suggestions. Thank you to Middlesex County College for their support in this project and to the students who beta tested the project to help make it better for future students.

Finally, my special thanks to all my former students who have given me insight and pleasure in developing this material.

J.H.

If you have questions or problems please e-mail Hochbaum@comcast.net

Basic Handling of CD

DO:

1. Handle discs by the outer edge or the center hold. Your fingerprints may be acidic enough to damage the disc.
2. Keep the discs clean. Wipe with cotton fabric in a straight line from the center of the disc toward the outer edge. If you wipe in a circle, any scratches may follow the tracks of the CD, rendering them unreadable.
3. Return discs to their plastic cases immediately after use.
4. Store discs in their cases in a cool, dry, dark place with clean air.

DO NOT:

1. Touch the surface of the disc.
2. Bend the disc.
3. Use adhesive labels.
4. Expose discs to extreme heat, high humidity or rapid temperature or humidity changes.
5. Spill soda on disc.
6. Scratch the label side of the disc. It's more sensitive than the transparent side.
7. Use a pen, pencil, or fine-tip marker to write on the disc.

Computer Requirements

Make sure that the PC monitor is set to a minimum of 16 bit color and display screen area is 800 x 600 dpi, or images will appear washed out (lacking color). To set monitor:

1. Go to settings
2. Control panel
3. Display
4. Settings (select 16 bit (minimum) or higher color.
5. Display area on screen set to 800 x 600 dpi.

How to Use the <u>Anatomy CD-ROM</u>

1. Insert the <u>Anatomy CD-ROM</u> into a CD-ROM drive.

2. The <u>Anatomy CD-ROM</u> should self launch and the Extensis Portfolio Browser should come up.

3. If the <u>Anatomy CD-ROM</u> does not self launch.

    a. Double click on My Computer.
    b. Double click on the icon called "AnatImages".
    c. Double click on the green icon image "anatomy".
    d. Extensis Portfolio Browser will open.
    e. Anatomical Images will appear. (See the picture below)

4. After the <u>Anatomy CD –Rom</u> has launched on your computer make sure that the **Toolbar** row is now visible. (See the picture below)

5. If the Toolbar is not visible go to **View** and select **Toolbar.**

6. If you want to view all 725 images at once go to **Catalogue** on the **Toolbar** and click on **Find All (Ctr'l + Shift + F)**

7. If you want to review specific anatomical images, type in the specific *Quick Find Word* for those images in the *Quick Find Box (White Space)*. Hit return and those anatomical thumb nail images will be displayed. (See the picture below)

8. The *Quick Find Word* is located on the **Question & Answer Quick Index** on **Page 7 for A&P I** and **Page 143 for A&P II** in the <u>**Question & Answer (Q &A)**</u> *Book.*

Toolbar

Quick Find Box

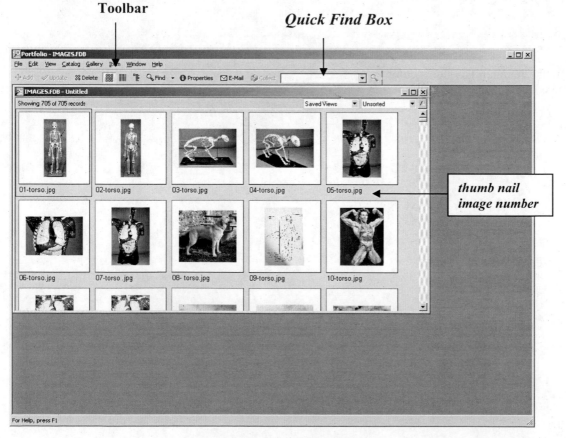

thumb nail image number

9. Each anatomical **thumbnail image** has a **number** followed by title (05-Torso.jpg) specific for that image. (See picture on the previous page)

10. To view and enlarge one thumbnail image at a time:

    a. Place the pointer on the specific anatomical thumbnail image and left double click on it with the mouse.

11. Located on the upper left of the screen (as you are looking at it) there are three icons that allow you to enlarge or decrease the images to better see the parts. (See the picture below).

    a. To Enlarge Image: Click on the Magnifying glass with + (plus) or double crossed arrows
    b. To Decrease Image: Click on the Magnifying glass with – (minus)

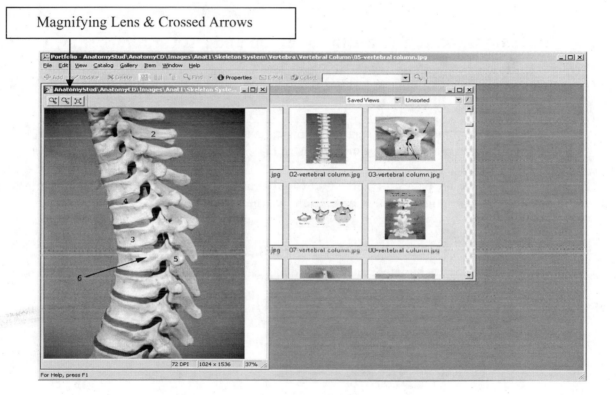

How to Use the Q&A (Question &Answer) Book

1. **The 1st part of the Q&A Book is for A&P I**

    a. The first set of White Pages is for A&P I anatomical image questions.
    b. The first set of White Pages with Gray Background is for A&P I anatomical image answers.

2. **The 2nd part of the Q &A Book is for A&P II**

    a. The second set of White Pages is for A&P II anatomical image questions.
    b. The second set of White Pages with Gray Background is for A&P II anatomical image answers.

3. **An example of how to use the question and answer tables shown below.**

    a. Launch the Anatomy CD-ROM and in this example type in the **Quick Find Word: Torso. Hit Enter Twice.**

    b. Several pictures will appear on your monitor. Locate **Torso** picture #01 (01-Torso.jpg) The **thumbnail image number** is right below the picture.

    c. Locate the pages for **Torso Questions** using the **Question and Answer Quick Find Index** on **page 7 for A &P I** in the **White pages.**

    d. Answer each question associated with the picture.

    e. Click on each picture on Torso and answer the questions associated with each one.

    f. On the same **Question and Answer Quick Find Index** locate the pages for **Torso Answers** in the White Pages with Gray Background.

White Pages

Topic (Anatomical position)
Quick Find Word: Torso

Picture #	Question #	Questions
01	1	Identify the side (left or right) of the body numbered 1.

White Pages with Gray Background

TORSO

Picture #	Question #	Answers
01	1	left

Question and Answer **Quick Find** Index
A & P I
Type in the Quick Find Word and Hit Enter Twice!

Images to view	Quick Find Word	Question pages	Answer pages	Images to view	Quick Find Word	Question pages	Answer pages
Anatomical position (torso)	Torso	10-11	77-78	Skeletal system (fibula)	Fibula	42	107-108
Ear	Ear	73-74	139-140	Skeletal system (foot)	Foot	42-43	108-109
Epithelial cell models	Epith model	12	79	Skeletal system (hand)	Hand	35-36	101-102
Eye	Eye	71-73	138-138	Skeletal system (humerus)	Humerus	31-33	97-99
Histology (bone)	Bone hist	44	109	Skeletal system individual vertebra	Individual	27	94
Histology connective tissue	Connect	13-14	80-81	Skeletal system (lumbar vertebra)	Lumbar	26	93
Histology epithelial tissue	Epithelium	12-13	79-80	Skeletal system (patella)	Patella	41	106
Histology (muscles)	Musclehist	58	124	Skeletal system (pelvic bone)	Pelvic Bone	37-38	102-103
Histology (nervous system	Nervehist	71	136-137	Skeletal system (pelvic girdle)	Pelvic Girdle	38-39	104
Joints (articulation)	Joint	44-46	109-111	Skeletal system (radius and ulna)	Radius	35	101
Muscles (human skeletal pictures)	Musclepict	46-53	111-118	Skeletal system (radius)	Radius	34	100
Muscles (human plastic models)	Humanplastic	53-57	119-122	Skeletal system (ribs)	Ribs	29	95-96
Nervous system brain stem models	Brainstem	66-67	132-133	Skeletal system sacrum &coccyx	Sacrum	27	93-94
Nervous system (brain ventricle models)	Brainvent	67-68	133	Skeletal system (scapula)	Scapula	30-31	96-97
Nervous system (human brain models)	Human brain	65-66	130-132	Skeletal system (skull)	Skull	15-23	82-89
Nervous system (neuron)	Neuron	58-61	124-127	Skeletal system (sternum)	Sternum	28-29	94-95
Nervous system (sheep brain)	Sheepbrain	61-64	127-130	Skeletal system (Thoracic vertebra)	Thoracic	25-26	92-93
Nervous system (spinal cord models)	Spinalcord	68-71	134-136	Skeletal system (tibia)	Tibia	41-42	106-107
Skeletal system (basic bone structure)	Basic bone	15	82	Skeletal system (ulna)	Ulna	33-34	99
Skeletal system (cervical vertebra)	Cervical	24-25	90-92	Skeletal system ulna/radius/hand	Hand	36	102
Skeletal system (clavicle)	Clavicle	30	96	Skeletal system vertebral column	Vertebral Column	23	89-90
Skeletal system (femur)	Femur	39-40	105-106	Skin	Skin	14	81

Human Anatomy & Physiology I
Laboratory Images
For
Student Review

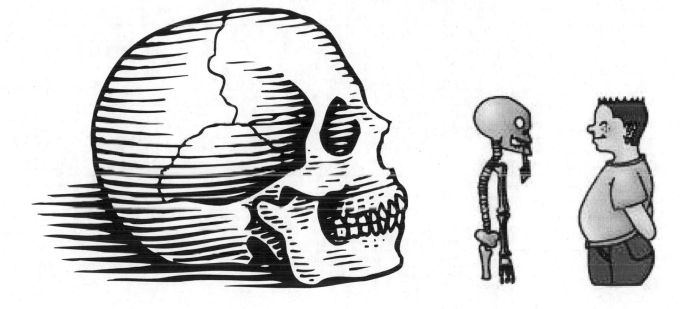

Picture #	Question #	Questions
01	1	Identify the side (left or right) of the body numbered 1.
	2	Identify the side (left or right) of the body numbered 2.
	3	Why is the skeleton NOT in correct anatomical position?
02	1	Identify the side (left or right) of the body numbered 1
	2	Identify the side (left or right) of the body numbered 2
03	1	Identify the anatomical surface of the cat numbered 1.
	2	Identify the anatomical surface of the cat numbered 2.
	3	Identify the anatomical surface of the cat numbered 3.
	4.	Identify the anatomical surface of the cat numbered 4.
	5.	Identify the leg (right or left) and surface numbered 5.
04	1	Identify the leg (right or left) and surface numbered 1.
	2	Identify the leg (right or left) and surface numbered 2.
05	1	Identify the anatomical surface of the lung numbered 1.
	2.	Identify the anatomical surface of the lung numbered 2.
	3.	Identify the anatomical surface of the lung numbered 3.
	4.	Identify the anatomical surface of the lung numbered 4.
	5.	Identify the anatomical surface of lung numbered 5.
	6	Identify left or right for this lung. Numbered 6
06	1	Identify the anatomical space numbered 1.
	2.	Identify the anatomical surface of the lung numbered 2.
	3.	Identify the anatomical surface of the liver numbered 3.
	4	Identify the anatomical surface of the lung numbered 4
	5	Identify left or right for the lung. Numbered 5
07	1	Identify the region of nine-numbered 1.
	2.	Identify the region of nine numbered 2.
	3.	Identify the region of nine numbered 3.
	4.	Identify the region of nine numbered 4.
	5.	Identify the region of nine numbered 5.
	6.	Identify the region of nine numbered 6.
08	1	Identify the dog's leg (left or right) and anatomical surface numbered 1.
	2	Identify the 's leg (left of right) and anatomical surface numbered 2.
09	A	Identify the frontal or coronal anatomical plane?
	B	Determine which is a sagittal or parasagittal anatomical plane?
	C	Determine which is a transverse anatomical plane?
	D	Determine which is a midsagittal anatomical plane?
10	A	Identify the region of nine marked A.
	B	Identify the region of nine marked B
	C	Identify the region of nine-marked C.
	D	Identify the region of nine-marked D.
	E	Identify the region of nine-marked E.
	F	Identify the region of nine-marked F.
11	1	Identify the specific cavity numbered 1 (light green).
12	1	Identify the abdominopelvic quadrant numbered 1
	2	Identify the abdominopelvic quadrant numbered 2
	3	Identify the abdominopelvic quadrant numbered 3
	4	Identify the abdominopelvic quadrant numbered 4
13	1	Identify the common name and anatomical term for the structure numbered 1.
	2	Identify the common name and anatomical term for the structure numbered 2.
	3	Identify the common name and anatomical term for the structure numbered 3.
	4	Identify the common name and anatomical term for the structure numbered 4.

	5	Identify the common name and anatomical term for the structure numbered 5.
	6	Identify the common name and anatomical term for the structure numbered 6.
	7	Identify the common name and anatomical term for the structure numbered 7.
	8	Identify the common name and anatomical term for the structure numbered 8.
	9	Identify the common name and anatomical term for the structure numbered 9.
	10	Identify the common name and anatomical term for the structure numbered 10.
	11	Identify the common name and anatomical term for the structure numbered 11.
	12	Identify the common name and anatomical term for the structure numbered 12.
	13	Identify the common name and anatomical term for the structure numbered 13.
	14	Identify the common name and anatomical term for the structure numbered 14.
	15	Give the name and number for the structure numbered 15.
	16	Identify the common name and anatomical term for the structure numbered 16.
	17	Identify the common name and anatomical term for the structure numbered 17.
	18	Identify the name and number for the structure numbered 18.
	19	Give the common name and anatomical term and number for the structure numbered 19.
	20	Identify the common name and anatomical term for the structure numbered 20.
14	1	Identify the leg (left or right) of the body numbered 1.
	2	Identify the arm (left or right) of the body numbered 2.
	3	Identify the leg (left or right) of the body numbered 3.
	4	Identify the arm (left or right) of the body numbered 4.
	5	Identify the anatomical surface of the leg numbered 5.
	6	Identify the anatomical surface of the leg numbered 6
	7	Identify the anatomical surface of the hand numbered 7.
	8	Identify the anatomical surface of the hand numbered 8.
	9	Identify the anatomical surface of the arm numbered 9.
	10	Identify the anatomical surface of the arm numbered 10.
	11	Identify the anatomical surface of the foot numbered 11.
	12	Identify the anatomical surface of the foot numbered 12.
	13	Describe the position of the area of the arm marked "A" in anatomical relationship to the area marked "B".
15	1	Identify the surface numbered 1 on the lung.
	2	Identify the surface numbered 2 on the lung.
	3	Identify the surface numbered 3 on the lung.
	4	Identify the surface numbered 4 on the lung.
	5	Organ number 5 is a : a. right lung b. left lung
	6	Identify the anatomical space numbered 6 on the torso.
16	1	Identify the specific abdominopelvic quadrant numbered 1.
	2	Identify the specific abdominopelvic quadrant numbered 2.
	3	Identify the specific abdominopelvic region of nine numbered 3.
	4	Identify the specific abdominopelvic region of nine numbered 4.
	5	Identify the specific abdominopelvic region of nine numbered 5.
	6	Identify the specific abdominopelvic region of nine numbered 6.
	7	Identify the specific serous (whitish) membrane numbered 7.
	8	Identify the specific serous membrane numbered 8.

EPITHELIAL CELL (MODELS)
Type **EPITH MODEL** in white space in tool bar to bring up these images

Picture #	Question #	Question
01	1	Identify the specific epithelial cell numbered 1.
	2	Identify the specific structure (organelle) numbered 2.
02	1	Identify the specific epithelial cell numbered 2.
	2	Identify the specific structure (organelle) numbered 2.
03	1	Identify the specific epithelial cell numbered 1.
	2	Identify the specific structure (organelle) numbered 2.
	3	Identify the specific arrangement of this epithelium.
04	1	Identify the specific epithelial cell numbered 1.
	2	Identify the specific cell modification numbered 2.
	3	Identify the specific arrangement of this epithelium.

EPITHELIAL HISTOLOGY (PICTURES)
Type **EPITHELIUM** in white space in tool bar to bring up these images

Picture #	Question #	Question
01	1	Identify the tissue labeled "A".
	2	Identify the specific cell type numbered 2.
02	1	Identify the specific cell type on this numbered 1.
	2	Identify the specific structure numbered 2.
03	1	Identify the tissue labeled "B".
	2	Identify the specific cell type numbered 2.
	3	Identify the cell arrangement.
	4	Identify the organelle numbered 4.
04	1	Identify the specific cell type numbered 1.
	2	Identify the specific cell (clear in appearance) numbered 2.
05	1	Identify the specific tissue numbered "C" (give complete name).
	2	Identify the area numbered 2.
06	1	Identify the cell type and arrangement of the tongue numbered 1.
07	1	Identify the specific cell type numbered 1.
	2	Identify the specific organelle numbered 2.
08	1	Identify the specific epithelial cell numbered 1.
	2	Identify the arrangement of the epithelial tissue lettered "D"
	3	Identify the cell surface numbered 3.
	4	Identify the cell surface numbered 4.
09	1	Identify the epithelium lettered "E".

	2	Identify the extracellular layer numbered 2.
10	1	Identify the epithelium cell numbered 1.
11	1	Identify the finger like structure numbered 1.
12	1	Identify the specific tissue lettered "F".
	2	Identify the specific cell numbered 2.
	3	Identify the specific cell numbered 3.
13	1	Identify the specific tissue numbered 13.
14	1	Identify the specific tissue lettered "G"
	2	Identify the structure numbered 2.
15	1	Identify the specific tissue numbered 1.

CONNECTIVE TISSUE HISTOLOGY
Type **CONNECTIVE** in white space in tool bar to bring up these images

Picture #	Question #	Question
01	1	Identify the specific tissue lettered "A"
	2	Identify the fiber numbered 2.
	3	Identify the fiber numbered 3
02	1	Is the tissue letter "B" an example of (loose, dense or specialized) tissue?
	2	Identify the specific fiber numbered 2.
03	1	Identify the specific tissue lettered "C".
	2	Identify the specific fiber numbered 2.
04	1	Identify the specific tissue lettered "D"
05	1	Is tissue lettered "E" and example of (loose, irregular dense, regular dense, or specialized) connective tissue?
06	1	Identify the specific fiber numbered 1.
07	1	Identify the tissue lettered "F".
08	1	Identify the specific tissue lettered "G".
	2	Identify the structure (white space) numbered 2.
	3	Identify the specific cell numbered 3.
09	1	Identify the specific tissue lettered "H"
	2	Identify the structure (space) numbered 2.
	3	Identify the specific cell numbered 3.
	4	Identify the specific part of the tissue numbered 4.
10	1	Identify the specific tissue lettered "I".
11	1	Identify the specific tissue lettered "J".
12	1	Identify the specific tissue lettered "K'.
	2	Identify the structure numbered 2.
	3	Identify the specific cell numbered 3.

13	1	Identify the specific structure numbered 1.
	2	Identify the specific structure numbered 2.
14	1	Identify the specific cell numbered 1.
	2	Identify the specific structure (thin black lines) numbered 2.
	3	Identify the specific structure numbered 3.
	4	Identify the specific passageway numbered 4.
15	1	Identify the specific tissue numbered 1.
16	1	Identify the specific cell numbered 1.
	2	Identify the structure (thin dark lines) numbered 2.
	3	Identify the specific structure numbered 3.
17	1	Identify this specific tissue lettered "L"
	2	Identify the part (green) numbered 2.
	3	Identify the entire structure numbered 3.
18	1	Identify the specific tissue lettered "M".
	2	Identify the structure (space) numbered 2.
	3	Identify the specific cell numbered 3.
19	1	Identify the specific tissue lettered "N".
	2	Identify the specific cell numbered 2.
20	1	Identify the tissue numbered 1.
21	1	Identify the specific cell crowed between the collagenous fibers numbered 1.

INTEGUMENTARY SYSTEM (SKIN)
Type **SKIN** in white space in tool bar to bring up these images

Picture #	Question #	Question
01	1	Identify the specific layer numbered 1.
	2	Identify the entire layer numbered 2.
	3	Identify the peglike projection numbered 3.
	4	Identify the specific region (layer) numbered 4.
	5	Identify the specific region (layer) numbered 5.
	6	Identify the structure numbered 6.
	7	Identify the specific gland numbered 7.
	8	Identify the specific smooth muscle numbered 8.
	9	Identify the specific structure numbered 9.
	10	Identify the specific structure numbered 10.
	11	Identify the tissue numbered 11.
	12	Identify the specific receptor numbered 12
	13	Identify the specific receptor numbered 13.
	14	Identify the layer numbered 14.
	15	Identify the layer numbered 15.

BASIC BONE STRUCTURE
Type **BASIC bone** white space in tool bar to bring up these images

Picture #	Question #	Question
01	1	Identify the basic part of a long bone numbered 1.
	2	Identify the basic part of a long bone numbered 2.
	3	Identify the basic part of a long bone numbered 3.
02	1	Identify the bone architecture numbered 1 located on the outside.
	2	Identify the bone architecture numbered 2 locate on the inside that appears honeycomb.
	2A	What specific type of connective tissue will be located within the spaces associated within the honeycomb architecture of bone architecture numbered 2?
	3	Identify the space located within the shaft
03	1	Identify the space numbered 1.
	2	Identify the bone architecture numbered 2 located on the outside.

AXIAL SKELETON
SKULL
Type **SKULL** in white space in tool bar to bring up these images

Picture #	Question #	Question
01	1	Identify the suture numbered 1.
	2	Identify the suture numbered 2
	3	Identify the bone numbered 3
	4	Identify the bone numbered 4
02	1	Identify the suture numbered 1
	2	Identify the suture numbered 2
	3	Identify the bone numbered 3.
	4	Identify the bone numbered 4
03	1	Identify the suture numbered 1
	2	Identify the suture numbered 2
	3	Identify the suture numbered 3
	4	Identify the yellow bone numbered 4
	5	Identify the green bone numbered 5
	6	Identify the blue bone numbered 6
04	1	Identify the brown bone numbered 1
	2	Identify the blue bone numbered 2
	3	Identify the green bone numbered 3
	4	Identify the yellow bone numbered 4

	5	Identify the suture numbered 5
	6	Identify the suture numbered 6
05	1	Identify the yellow bone numbered 1
	2	Identify the yellow bone numbered 2
	3	Identify the purple bone numbered 3
	4	Identify the white bone numbered 4
	5	Identify the orange bone numbered 5
	6	Identify the process numbered 6
	7	Identify the process numbered 7
	8	Identify the process numbered 8
	9	Identify the process numbered 9
	10	Identify the fissure (slit) numbered 10
	11	Identify the foramen numbered 11
	12	Identify the suture numbered 12
	13	Identify the yellow bone numbered 13
06	1	Identify the bone numbered 1
	2	Identify the bone numbered 2
07	1	Identify the hole numbered 1
	2	Identify the slit numbered 2
	3	Identify the slit numbered 3
	4	Identify the hole numbered 4
	5	Identify the bone numbered 5
	6	Identify the hole numbered 6
	7	Identify the bone numbered 7
	8	Identify the bone numbered 8
	9	Identify the bone numbered 9
	10	Identify the bones numbered 10
	11	Identify the bone numbered 11
	12	Identify the bone numbered 12
08		Identify the bone in this picture
09	1	Identify the bone numbered 1
	2	Identify the bone numbered 2
	3	Identify the bone numbered 3
	4	Identify the slit numbered 4
	5	Identify the bone numbered 5
	6	Identify the bone numbered 6
10	1	Identify the yellow bone numbered 1
	2	Identify the green bone numbered 2

	3	Identify the blue bone numbered 3
	4	Identify the brown portion and bone numbered 4
	5	Identify the orange portion and bone numbered 5
	6	Identify the yellow bone numbered 6
	7	Identify the purple bone numbered 7
	8	Identify the yellow-orange bone numbered 8
	9	Identify the white bone numbered 9
	10	Identify the long slender process numbered 10
	11	Identify the orange process numbered 11
	12	Identify the brown rounded process numbered 12
	13	Identify the opening numbered 13
11	1	Identify the yellow bone numbered 1
	2	Identify the white bone numbered 2
	3	Identify the purple bone numbered 3
	4	Identify the yellow-brown bone numbered 4
	5	Identify the yellow bone numbered 5
	6	Identify the orange bone numbered 6
12	1	Identify the process numbered 1
	2	Identify the hole numbered 2
	3	Identify the bone numbered 3
	4	Identify the slit numbered 4
	5	Identify the bone numbered 5
	6	Identify the bone numbered 6
13	1	Identify the bone numbered 1
	2	Identify the bone numbered 2
	3	Identify the process and bone numbered 3
	4	Identify the process numbered 4
	5	Identify the process and bone numbered 5
	6	Identify the bone numbered 6
	7	Identify the process and bone numbered 7
14	1	Identify the part numbered 1
	2	Identify the process numbered 2
	3	Identify the process numbered 3
	4	Identify the part numbered 4
	5	Identify the part of the tooth numbered 5
	6	Identify the part of the tooth numbered 6
	7	Identify the hole numbered 7
15	1	Identify the process numbered 1

	2	Identify the process numbered 2
	3	Identify the hole numbered 3
	4	Identify the process numbered 4
	5	Identify the type of named by location numbered 5
16	1	Identify the bone numbered 1
	2	Identify the bone numbered 2
17	1	Identify the depression numbered 1
	2	Identify the rounded process numbered 2
	3	Identify the process numbered 3
	4	Identify the process numbered 4
	5	Identify the part numbered 5
	6	Identify the hole numbered 6
18	1	Identify the process numbered 1
	2	Identify the hole numbered 2
	3	Identify the hole
	4	Identify the bone numbered 4
	5	Identify the process numbered 5
19	1	Identify the hole numbered 1
	2	Identify the long slender process numbered 2
	3	Identify the round process numbered 3
	4	Identify the process numbered 4
	5	Identify the process and bone numbered 5
	6	Identify the process numbered 6
	7	Identify the process and bone numbered 7
	8	Identify the bone numbered 8
20	1	Identify the hole numbered 1
	2	Identify the process numbered 2
	3	Identify the depression numbered 3
	4	Identify the hole numbered 4
	5	Identify the hole numbered 5
	6	Identify the hole numbered 6
	7	Identify the hole numbered 7
	8	Identify the process and bone numbered 8
	9	Identify the process and bone numbered 9
	10	Identify the blue bone numbered 10
	11	Identify the process numbered 11
	12	Identify the anatomical part of the brown bone numbered 12
21	1	Identify the hole numbered 1
	2	Identify the hole numbered 2

	3	Identify the anatomical part numbered 3
	4	Identify the hole numbered 4
	5	Identify the hole numbered 5
	6	Identify the hole numbered 6
	7	Identify the process and bone numbered 7
	8	Identify the process and bone numbered 8
	9	Identify the depression numbered 9
	10	Identify the process and bone numbered 10
	11	Identify the hole numbered 11
	12	Identify the bone numbered 12
	13	Identify the rounded process numbered 13
	14	Identify the bone numbered 14
	15	Identify the process and bone numbered 15
22	1	Identify the hole numbered 1
	2	Identify the hole numbered 2
	3	Identify the hole numbered 3
	4	Identify the hole numbered 4
	5	Identify the depression numbered 5
	6	Identify the process numbered 6
	7	Identify the bone numbered 7
23	1	Identify the hole numbered 1
	2	Identify the rounded process numbered 2
	3	Identify the process numbered 3
	4	Identify the hole numbered 4
	5	Identify the hole numbered 5
	6	Identify the hole numbered 6
	7	Identify the hole numbered 7
	8	Identify the depression numbered 8
	9	Identify the bone numbered 9
	10	Identify the bone numbered 10
	11	Identify the hole numbered 11
24	1	Identify the hole numbered 1
	2	Identify the hole numbered 2
	3	Identify the hole numbered 3
	4	Identify the hole numbered 4
	5	Identify the process and bone numbered 5
	6	Identify the process and bone numbered 6
	7	Identify the" trough-shaped" process numbered 7

25	1	Identify the bone
	2	Identify the process numbered 2
	3	Identify the pointed process numbered 3
26	1	Identify the process numbered 1
	2	Identify the rounded process numbered 2
	3	Identify the part numbered 3
	4	Identify the hole numbered 4
	5	Identify the part of the mandible numbered 5
	6	Identify the part numbered 6
	7	Identify the part of the body numbered 7
27	1	Identify the part of body numbered 1
	2	Identify the part numbered 2
	3	Identify the hole numbered 3
	4	Identify the border numbered 4
	5	Identify the part numbered 5
28	1	Identify the part numbered 1
	2	Identify the hole numbered 2
	3	Identify the hole numbered 3
	4	Identify the process numbered 4
29	1	Identify the process and bone numbered 1
	2	Identify the bone numbered 2
	3	Identify the hole numbered 3
	4	Identify the hole numbered 4
	5	Identify the bone numbered 5
	6	Identify the bone numbered 6
30	1	Identify the bone numbered 1
	2	Identify the pointed structure numbered 2
	3	Identify the part numbered 3
	4	Identify the hole numbered 4
	5	Identify the anatomical portion and bone numbered 5
	6	Identify the depression numbered 6
	7	Identify the hole numbered 7
	8	Identify the anatomical portion and bone numbered 8
	9	Identify the hole numbered 9
	10	Identify the bone numbered 10
	11	Identify the hole numbered 11
31	1	Identify the pointed process numbered 1
	2	Identify the bone numbered 2
	3	Identify the hole numbered 3

	4	Identify the hole numbered 4
	5	Identify the depression numbered 5
	6	Identify the hole numbered 6
	7	Identify the hole numbered 7 along rim of foramen magnum
	8	Identify the hole numbered 8
	9	Identify the anatomical part and bone numbered 9
32	1	Identify the process numbered 1
	2	Identify the hole numbered 2
	3	Identify the hole numbered 3
	4	Identify the hole numbered 4
	5	Identify the hole numbered 5
	6	Identify the depression numbered 6
	7	Identify the part numbered 7
	8	Identify the holes numbered 8
	9	Identify the hole numbered 9
33	1	Identify the process numbered 1
	2	Identify the anatomical part numbered 2
	3	Identify the rounded process numbered 3
	4	Identify the hole numbered 4
	5	Identify the depression numbered 5
34	1	Identify the anatomical part numbered 1
	2	Identify the anatomical part numbered 2
	3	Identify the hole numbered 3
35	1	Identify the process numbered 1
	2	Identify the process numbered 2
	3	Identify the process numbered 3
	4	Identify the sinuses numbered 4
36		Where would these bones be located in the skull
37	1	Identify the process numbered 1
	2	Identify the process numbered 2
	3	Identify the sinuses numbered 3
	4	Identify the process numbered 4
38	1	Identify the holes numbered 1
	2	Identify the hole numbered 2
	3	Identify the part numbered 3
	4	Identify the hole numbered 4
	5	Identify the part of the sphenoid numbered 5
	6	Identify the depression numbered 6

	7	Identify the part of the sphenoid numbered 7
39	1	Identify the hole numbered 1
	2	Identify the bone numbered 2
	3	Identify the bone numbered 3
	4	Identify the hole numbered 4
40	1	Identify the process numbered 1
	2	Identify the pointed process numbered 2
	3	Identify the part of the ethmoid bone numbered 3
	4	Identify the bone numbered 4
	5	Identify the bone numbered 5
41	1	Identify the part numbered 1
	2	Identify the process numbered 2
	3	The part of the ethmoid numbered 3 will form which part of the skull
	4	Identify the process numbered 4
	5	Identify the part of the ethmoid numbered 5
42	1	Identify the process numbered 1
	2	Identify the hole numbered 2
	3	Identify the hole numbered 3
43	1	Identify the fontanel numbered 1
	2	Identify the suture numbered 2
	3	Identify the suture numbered 3
44	1	Identify the fontanel numbered 1
	2	Identify the fontanel numbered 2
45	1	Identify the fontanel numbered 1
	2	Identify the suture numbered 2
46	1	Identify the fontanel numbered 1
	2	Identify the suture numbered 2
	3	Identify the suture numbered 3
	4	Identify the suture numbered 4
47	1	Identify the bone numbered 1
48	1	Identify the bone numbered 1
	2	Identify the bone numbered 2
49	1	Identify the bone numbered 1 on the disarticulated skull
	2	Identify the bone numbered 2 on the disarticulated skull

VERTEBRAL COLUMN
Type **VERTEBRAL COL** in white space in tool bar to bring up these images

Picture #	Question #	Question
01	1	Identify the part of the vertebra numbered 1
	2	Identify the part of the vertebra numbered 2
	3	Identify the part of the vertebral column numbered 3
	4	Identify the bone of the vertebral column numbered 4
02	1	Identify the part of the vertebra numbered 1
	2	Identify the part of the vertebral column numbered 2
	3	Identify the part of the vertebra numbered 3
03	1	Identify the part of the vertebra numbered 1
	2	Identify the part of the vertebra numbered 2
	3	Identify the part of the vertebra numbered 3
	4	Identify the hole numbered 4
	5	Identify the part of the vertebra numbered 5
04	1	Identify the part of the vertebra numbered 1
	2	Identify the part of the vertebra numbered 2
	3	Identify the part of the vertebra numbered 3
	4	Identify the yellow structure numbered 4
05	1	Identify the hole numbered 1
	2	Identify the part numbered 2
	3	Identify the part numbered 3
	4	Identify the part numbered 4
	5	Identify the part numbered 5
	6	Identify the structure (depression) numbered 6
06	1	Identify the specific vertebra numbered 1
	2	Identify the group of vertebra numbered 2
	3	Identify the group of vertebra numbered 3
	4	Identify the group of vertebra numbered 4
	5	Identify the process numbered 5
	6	Identify the process numbered 6
07		Which vertebra has the largest body?
08		REVIEW POSTEIOR VEIW OF VERTEBRA SET
09		REVIEW LATERAL VIEW OF VERTEBRA SET
10	1	Identify the pointed structure numbered 1
	2	Identify the process numbered 2
	3	Identify the part numbered 3
11		REVIEW LATERAL VIEW OF VERTEBRAL COLUMN

CERVICAL VERTEBRA
Type **CERVICAL** in white space in tool bar to bring up these images

Picture #	Question #	Question
01	1	Identify the process numbered 1
	2	Identify the process numbered 2
	3	Identify the hole numbered 3
	4	Identify the part numbered 4
	5	What process articulates to the area numbered 5
	6	Identify this specific vertebra
02	1	Identify the process numbered 1
	2	Identify the part of the inferior arc numbered 2
	3	Identify the part numbered 3.
	4	Identify the hole numbered 4
	5	Identify the part numbered 5
	6	Identify the hole numbered 6
	7	Identify this specific vertebra
	8	Identify the part numbered 8
03	1	Identify the part numbered 1
	2	Identify the part numbered 2
	3	Identify the part of the superior arch numbered 3
	4	Identify the part numbered 4
	5	Identify the hole numbered 5
	6	Identify the hole numbered 6
	7	Identify the part of the superior arch numbered 7
	8	Identify the part numbered 8
	9	How do you know these are cervical vertebrae?
04	1	What part of the axis articulates to the area numbered 2?
	2	Identify the hole numbered 2
	3	Identify the part numbered 3
	4	Identify the part numbered 4
	5	Identify the part numbered 5
	6	Identify the part numbered 6
	7	Identify the part numbered 7
	8	Identify the part numbered 8
	9	Identify the part numbered 9
	10	Identify the part numbered 10
	11	What does the axis have that the atlas does not?
	12	What does the atlas **not** have that the axis does have?

05	1	Identify the part numbered 1
	2	Identify the hole numbered 2
	3	Identify the part numbered 3
	4	Identify the part numbered 4
	5	Identify the part numbered 5
	6	Identify the part numbered 6
	7	Identify the hole numbered 7
	8	Identify the part numbered 8
	9	Identify the part numbered 9
	10	Identify the hole numbered 10
06	1	Identify the part numbered 1
	2	Identify the part numbered 2
	3	Identify the part numbered 3
	4	Identify the part numbered 4
	5	Identify the hole numbered 5
	6	Identify the part numbered 6
	7	What attaches (articulates) to the part numbered 6
	8	Identify the part numbered 8
07	1	Identify the part numbered 1
	2	Identify the part numbered 2
	3	Identify the part numbered 3
08	1	Identify the part numbered 1
	2	Identify the part numbered 2
	3	Identify the part numbered 3
	4	Identify the part numbered 4
09		Review the shape of C1, C2, and C7
10		Review the shape of C1, C2, and C7
11	1	Identify the part numbered 1
	2	Identify the part numbered 2
	3	Identify the part numbered 3
	4	Identify this specific vertebra

THORACIC VERTEBRA
Type **THORACIC** in white space in tool bar to bring up these images

Picture #	Question #	Question
01	1	Identify the part numbered 1
	2	Identify the part numbered 2

	3	Identify the part numbered 3
	4	What specific bone part articulates to the part numbered 4?
	5	Identify the part numbered 5
	6	What organ is contained within the part numbered 6?
	7	What specific bone part articulates to the part numbered 7?
	8	What specific bone part articulates to the part numbered 8?
	9	Identify the part numbered 9
02	1	Identify the part numbered 1
	2	Identify the part numbered 2
	3	Identify the part numbered 3
	4	Identify the part numbered 4
	5	Identify the part numbered 5
	6	Identify the part numbered 6
	7	Identify the part numbered 7
03	1	Identify the part numbered 1
	2	Identify the part numbered 2
	3	Identify the part numbered 3
	4	Identify the part numbered 4
	5	Identify the part numbered 5
	6	Identify the part numbered 6
04	1	Identify the part numbered 1
	2	Identify the part numbered 2
	3	Identify the part numbered 3
	4	Identify the part numbered 4
	5	Identify the part numbered 5
	6	Identify the part numbered 6

LUMBAR VERTEBRA
Type **LUMBAR** in white space in tool bar to bring up these images

Picture #	Question #	Question
01	1	Identify the part numbered 1
	2	Identify the part numbered 2
	3	Identify the part numbered 3
	4	Identify the part numbered 4
	5	Identify the part numbered 5
	6	Identify the part numbered 6
	7	Identify the part numbered 7

SACRUM and COCCYX
Type **SACRUM** in white space in tool bar to bring up these images

Picture #	Question #	Question
01	1	Identify the part numbered 1
	2	Identify the part numbered 2
	3	Identify the hole numbered 3
	4	Identify the concave space numbered 4
	5	Identify the specific bone numbered 5
	6	Identify the surface on the bone numbered 6
02	1	Identify the area numbered 1
	2	Identify the hole numbered 2
	3	Identify the specific bone numbered 3
	4	Identify the part numbered 4
03	1	Identify the part numbered 1
	2	Identify the part numbered 2
	3	Identify the specific bone numbered 3
	4	Identify the part numbered 4
	5	What specific bone articulates to the area numbered 1
04	1	Identify the part numbered 1
	2	Identify the hole numbered 2
	3	Identify the part numbered 3

INDIVIDUAL VERTEBRA
Type **INDIVID** in white space in tool bar to bring up these images

Picture #	Question #	Question
01	1	Identify the specific bone numbered 1
02	1	Identify the bone numbered 1
	2	Identify the bone numbered 2
03	1	Identify this specific bone
04	1	Identify this specific bone
05	1	Identify this specific bone
O6	1	Identify this specific bone
07	1	Identify this specific bone

STERNUM

Type **STERNUM** in white space in tool bar to bring up these images

Picture #	Question #	Question
01	1	Identify the specific bone numbered 1
	2	Identify the specific bone numbered 2
	3	Identify the notch numbered 3
	4	Identify the notch numbered 4
	5	What specific structure articulates to the area numbered 5?
	6	What specific structure articulates to the area numbered 6?
02	1	Identify the notch numbered 1
	2	Identify the notch numbered 2
	3	What specific structure articulates to the area numbered 3?
	4	What specific bone articulates to the area numbered 4?
03	1	Identify the specific bone numbered1
	2	Identify the notches numbered 2
04	1	Identify the specific bone numbered 1
	2	Identify the notch numbered 2
	3	Identify the notch numbered 3
	4	What specific bone articulates to the area numbered 4
05	1	Identify the depression numbered 1 on the manubrium
	2	Identify the depression numbered 2 on the manubrium
	3	What specific structure articulates to the area numbered 3 on the manubrium
06	1	Identify the specific bone numbered 1
	2	Identify the area (junction) numbered 2
	3	Identify the notch numbered 3
	4	What specific bone articulates numbered 4
07	1	Identify the bone numbered 1
	2	Identify the bone numbered 2
	3	Identify the bone numbered 3
	4	Identify the bone numbered 4
08	1	Identify the bone numbered 1
	2	Identify the bone numbered 2
	3	Identify the bone numbered 3
	4	Identify the bone numbered 4
	5	Identify the specific bone numbered 5
	6	Identify the specific structure numbered 6
	7	Identify the specific bone numbered 7

	8	Identify the specific bone numbered 8
	9	How would you classify the rib numbered 8 above?
09	1	Identify the specific bone numbered 1
	2	Identify the specific bone numbered 2
	3	Identify the specific bone numbered 3
	4	Identify the structure numbered 4
	5	Identify the structure numbered 5
	6	Identify the bone numbered 6
	7	Identify the specific bone numbered 7

RIBS

Type **RIB** in white space in tool bar to bring up these images

Picture #	Question #	Question
01	1	Identify the specific structure numbered 1
	2	Identify the specific structure numbered 2
	3	Identify the specific structure numbered 3
	4	Identify the specific groove numbered 4
	5	Identify the specific structure numbered 5
	6	Identify the specific structure numbered 6
02	1	Identify the specific bone numbered A
	2	Identify the specific bone numbered B
	3	Identify the specific bone numbered C
	4	The costal cartilage marked D is attached to what class of ribs?
	5	The costal cartilage marked E is attached to what class of ribs?
03	1	Identify the area numbered 1 that the head of the rib articulates to:
	2	Identify the area numbered 2 that the tubercle of the rib articulates to:
04	1	Identify this specific bone
	2	Identify the part numbered 2
	3	Identify the part numbered 3
05	1	Which ribs are classified as true (vertebrosternal) ribs?
	2	Which ribs are classified as false (vertebrochondral) ribs?
	3	Which ribs are classified as floating (vertebral) ribs?
06	1	Identify the specific part numbered 1
	2	Identify the specific part numbered 2
	3	Identify the specific part numbered 3

CLAVICLE
Type **CLAVICLE** in white space in tool bar to bring up these images

Picture #	Question #	Question
01	1	Identify this bone
	2	Identify the part numbered 2
	3	Identify the part numbered 3
02	1	Identify this bone
	2	Identify the part numbered 2
	3	Identify the part numbered 3
03	1	Identify the specific bone numbered 1
	2	Identify the specific part numbered 2
	3	Identify the specific part numbered 3
	4	Identify the specific part numbered 4
	5	Identify the depression numbered 5
	6	Identify the depression numbered 6
04	1	Identify the part numbered 1
	2	Identify the part numbered 2

SCAPULA
Type **SCAPULA** in white space in tool bar to bring up these images

Picture #	Question #	Question
01	1	Identify the part numbered 1
	2	Identify the part numbered 2
	3	Identify the depression numbered 3
	4	Identify the depression numbered 4
	5	Identify the angel numbered 5
	6	Identify the border of the body numbered 6
	7	Identify the angle numbered 7
	8	Identify the border of the body numbered 8
	9	Identify the depression numbered 9
02	1	Identify the depression numbered 1
	2	Identify the process numbered 2
	3	Identify the process numbered 3
	4	Identify the fossa numbered 4
	5	Identify the part numbered 5
03	1	Identify the depression numbered 1

	2	Identify the part numbered 2
	3	Identify the part numbered 3
	4	Identify the depression numbered 4
	5	Identify the indentation numbered 5
04	1	Identify the part numbered 1
	2	Identify the part numbered 2
	3	Identify the depression numbered 3
	4	Identify the angle numbered 4
	5	Identify the angle numbered 5
	6	Identify the depression numbered 6
	7	Identify the border numbered 7
	8	Identify the border numbered 8
05	1	Identify this bone
	2	Determine left or right for this bone

HUMERUS
Type **HUMERUS** in white space in tool bar to bring up these images

Picture #	Question #	Question
01	1	Identify the process numbered 1
	2	Identify the process numbered 2
	3	Identify the specific part of the shaft numbered 3
	4	Identify the process numbered 4
	5	Identify the process numbered 5
	6	Identify the process numbered 6
	7	Identify the groove numbered 7
	8	Identify the process numbered 8
	9	Identify the depression numbered 9
	10	Identify the process numbered 10
	11	Identify the depression numbered 11
	12	Identify the roughened V-shaped area numbered 12 (hint: named after muscle that moves arm)
02	1	Identify the process numbered 1
	2	Identify the process numbered 2
	3	Identify the anatomical part numbered 3
	4	Identify the groove numbered 3
	5	Identify the process numbered 5
03	1	Identify the process numbered 1
	2	Identify the process numbered 2

	3	Identify the process numbered 3
	4	Identify the process numbered 4
	5	Identify the depression numbered 5
	6	Identify the depression numbered 6
	7	Identify the part of the bone numbered 5
	8	Identify the part of the bone numbered 6
04	1	Identify the process numbered 1
	2	Identify the process numbered 2
	3	Identify the process numbered 3
	4	Identify the groove numbered 4
	5	Identify the part numbered 5
	6	Identify the hole numbered 6
	7	Identify the groove numbered 7
05	1	Identify the process numbered 1
	2	Identify the process numbered 2
	3	Identify the process numbered 3
	4	Identify the groove numbered 4
	5	identify the anatomical area numbered 5
	6	Identify the groove numbered 6
06	1	Identify the process numbered 1
	2	Identify the process numbered 2
	3	Identify the process numbered 3
	4	Identify the process numbered 4
	5	Identify the area numbered 5
	6	Identify the depression numbered 6
	7	Identify the depression numbered 7
07	1	Identify the process numbered 1
	2	Identify the groove numbered 2
	3	Identify the process numbered 3
	4	Identify the bump on the shaft numbered 4
	5	Identify the area numbered 5
08	1	Identify the process numbered 1
	2	Identify the process numbered 2
	3	Identify the area numbered 3
	4	Identify the area numbered 4
	5	Identify the bump numbered 5
	6	Identify the process numbered 6
	7	Identify the process numbered 7

	8	Identify the process numbered 8
	9	Identify the depression numbered 9
09	1	Identify the process numbered 1
	2	Identify the process numbered 2
	3	Identify the process numbered 3
	4	Identify the depression numbered 4
10	1	Which bone is a right humerus
11	1	Which bone is a left humerus
12	1	Identify this bone
	2	Determine left or right for this bone

ULNA

Type **ULNA** in white space in tool bar to bring up these images

Picture #	Question #	Question
01	1	Identify the process numbered 1
	2	Identify the process numbered 2
	3	Identify the depression numbered 3
	4	Identify the process numbered 4
	5	Identify the process numbered 5
	6	Identify the depression numbered 6
02	1	Identify the process numbered 1
	2	Identify the indentation numbered 2
	3	Identify the process numbered 3
	4	Identify the process numbered 4
	5	Identify the pointed process numbered 5
	6	Identify the depression numbered 6
03	1	Identify the process numbered 1
	2	Identify the process numbered 2
	3	Identify the process (depression) numbered 3
	4	Identify the depression numbered 4
04	1	Identify the process numbered 1
	2	Identify the depression numbered 2
	3	Identify the process numbered 3
	4	Identify the large curved colored light green area numbered 4
05	1	Identify the process numbered 1
	2	Identify the process numbered 2
	3	Identify the process numbered 3

	4	Identify the curved depression numbered 4
06	1	Identify this bone
	2	Determine left or right for this bone

RADIUS
Type **RADIUS** in white space in tool bar to bring up these images

Picture #	Question #	Question
01	1	Identify the process numbered 1
	2	Identify the narrowed portion numbered 2
	3	Identify the raised process numbered 3
	4	Identify the pointed process numbered 4
	5	Identify the concave area numbered 5
02	1	Identify the rounded process numbered 1
	2	Identify the narrowed process numbered 2
	3	Identify the raised, roughened area numbered 3
	4	Identify the pointed process numbered 4
	5	What bones articulate to the area numbered 5
03	1	Identify the process numbered 1
	2	Identify the process numbered 2
	3	Identify the process numbered 3
	4	Identify the process numbered 4
04	1	Identify the process numbered 1
	2	Identify the process numbered 2
	3	Identify the process numbered 3
	4	Identify the concave area numbered 4
	5	Identify the pointed process numbered 5
05	1	Identify the process numbered 1
	2	Identify the process numbered 2
06	1	Identify the process numbered 1
	2	How can you determine this is an anterior view of the radius (besides that it is labeled anterior view)?
07	1	Identify this bone.
	2	Determine left or right for this bone

RADIUS and ULNA
Type **ULNARADIUS** in white space in tool bar to bring up these images

Picture #	Question #	Question
01	1	Identify the process numbered 1
	2	Identify the process numbered 2
	3	Identify the process numbered 3
	4	Identify the process numbered 4
	5	Identify the concave area numbered 5
	6	Identify the process numbered 6
	7	Identify the process numbered 7
02	1	Identify the process numbered 1
	2	Identify the process numbered 2
	3	Identify the process numbered 3
	4	Identify the concave depression numbered 4
	5	Identify the raised area on the diaphysis numbered 5
03	1	Identify the process numbered 1
	2	Identify the area numbered 2
	3	Identify the process numbered 3
	4	Identify the concave area numbered 4
	5	Identify the process numbered 5

HAND
Type **HAND** in white space in tool bar to bring up these images

Picture #	Question #	Question
01	1	Identify the specific part and bone number that is numbered 1
	2	Identify the specific part and bone number that is numbered 2
	3	Identify the specific part and bone number that is numbered 3
	4	Identify the specific part and bone number that is numbered 4
	5	Identify the specific part and bone number that is numbered 5
	6	Identify the specific part and bone number that is numbered 6
	7	Identify the specific part and bone number that is numbered 7
	8	Identify the specific part and bone number that is numbered 8
	9	Identify the specific part and bone number that is numbered 9
	10	Identify the specific bone numbered 10
	11	The "thumb" is phalanx number?
02	1	Identify the specific bone number that is numbered 1

	2	Identify the specific part and bone number that is numbered
	3	Identify the specific part and bone number that is numbered 3
	4	Identify the specific part and bone number that is numbered
	5	Identify the specific part and bone number that is numbered 5
	6	Identify the specific part and bone number that is numbered 6
	7	Identify the specific part and bone number that is numbered 7
	8	Identify the specific part and bone number that is numbered 8
	9	Identify the specific part and bone number that is numbered 9
	10	Identify the specific part and bone number that is numbered 10
	11	Identify the specific part and bone number that is numbered 11
	12	Identify the specific part and bone number that is numbered 12
	13	Identify the specific part and bone number that is numbered 13
	14	Identify the specific part and bone number that is numbered 14
	15	Identify the specific part and bone number that is numbered 15
	16	Identify the specific part and bone number that is numbered 16
	17	Identify the specific part and bone number that is numbered 17
	18	Identify the specific part and bone number that is numbered 18
	19	Identify the specific part and bone number that is numbered 19
	20	Identify the group of bones numbered 20
03	1	Identify the specific bone numbered 1
	2	Identify the specific bone numbered 2
	3	Identify the specific bone numbered 3
	4	Identify the specific bone numbered 4
	5	Identify the specific bone numbered 5
	6	Identify the group of bones numbered 6

ULNA, RADIUS and HAND

Type **ULNARADHAND** in white space in tool bar to bring up these images

Picture #	Question #	Question
01	1	Identify the bone numbered 1
	2	Identify the bone numbered 2
02	1	Identify the part and bone numbered 1
	2	Identify the part and bone numbered 2
	3	Identify the process numbered 3
	4	Identify the process numbered 4

PELVIC (HIP) BONE
Type **PELVIC BONE** in white space in tool bar to bring up these images

Picture #	Question #	Question
01	1	Identify the curved area numbered 1
	2	Identify the pointed structure numbered 2
	3	Identify the pointed structure numbered 3
	4	Identify the pointed structure numbered 4
	5	Identify the pointed structure numbered 5
	6	Identify the pointed structure numbered 6
	7	Identify the concave structure numbered 7
	8	Identify the rough process numbered 8
	9	Identify the anatomical division numbered 9
	10	Identify the anatomical division numbered 10
	11	Identify the hole numbered 11
	12	Identify the indentation numbered 12
	13	Identify the indentation numbered 13
02	1	Identify the pointed structure numbered 1
	2	Identify the pointed structure numbered 2
	3	Identify the pointed structure numbered 3
	4	Identify the pointed structure numbered 4
	5	Identify the pointed structure numbered 5
	6	Identify the anatomical division numbered 6
	7	Identify the anatomical division numbered 7
	8	Identify the anatomical division numbered 8
	9	Identify the concave depression numbered 9
	10	Identify the curved part numbered 10
	11	Identify the hole numbered 11
	12	Identify the indentation numbered 12
	13	Identify the indentation numbered 13
	14	Identify the rough looking projection numbered 14
03	1	Identify the anatomical division in red
	2	Identify the anatomical division in blue
	3	Identify the anatomical division in green
04	1	Identify the curved area numbered 1
	2	Identify the anatomical division numbered 2
	3	Identify the pointed structure numbered 3
	4	Identify the pointed structure numbered 4
	5	Identify the pointed structure numbered 5

	6	Identify the pointed structure numbered 6
	7	Identify the pointed structure numbered 7
	8	The joint formed between two hip bones at the area numbered 8 is:
	9	Identify the area numbered 9
	10	Identify the anatomical area numbered 10
	11	Identify the hole numbered 11
	12	Identify the rough area numbered 12
	13	Identify the indentation numbered 13
	14	Identify the indentation numbered 14
05	1	Identify this bone
	2	Determine if this bone is a left or right.

PELVIC GIRDLE
Type **PELVIC GIRDLE** in white space in tool bar to bring up these images

Picture #	Question #	Question
01	1	Identify the curved ridge numbered 1
	2	Identify the concave depression numbered 1
	3	Identify the pointed structure numbered 3
	4	Identify the area numbered 4
	5	Identify the pointed structure numbered 5
	6	Identify the structure numbered 6
	7	Identify the pointed structure numbered 7
	8	Identify the concave depression numbered 8
	9	Identify the hole numbered 9
	10	Identify the bone numbered 10
	11	Identify the bone numbered 11
02	1	Identify the pelvis marked in purple
	2	Identify the pelvis marked in black
03	1	Identify the curved ridge numbered 1
	2	Identify the pointed structure numbered 2
	3	Identify the pointed structure numbered 3
	4	Identify the bone numbered 4
	5	Identify the bone numbered 5
	6	Identify the rough process numbered 6
	7	Identify the hole numbered 7
	8	Identify the anatomical division numbered 8
	9	Identify the concave indentation numbered 9

	10	Identify the pointed structure numbered 10
04	1	Identify the curved ridge numbered 1
	2	Identify the pointed structure numbered 2
	3	Identify the pointed structure numbered 3
	4	Identify the concave structure numbered 4
	5	Identify the pointed structure numbered 5
	6	Identify the anatomical division numbered 6
	7	Identify the process numbered 7
	8	Identify the bone numbered 8
	9	Identify the anatomical division numbered 9
	10	Identify the concave indentation numbered 10
	11	Identify the hole numbered 11

FEMUR

Type **FEMUR** in white space in tool bar to bring up these images

Picture #	Question #	Question
01	1	Identify the rounded process numbered 1
	2	Identify the process numbered 2
	3	Identify the process numbered 3
	4	Identify the pointed process numbered 4
	5	Identify the process numbered 5
	6	Identify the process numbered 6
	7	Identify the smooth concave area numbered 7
02	1	Identify the part numbered 1
	2	Identify the part numbered 2
	3	Identify the part numbered 3
	4	Identify the part numbered 4
	5	Identify the long rough raised vertical ridge located on the shaft numbered 5
	6	Identify the rounded process numbered 6
	7	Identify the rounded process numbered 7
	8	Identify the depression located between part numbers 6 and 7 numbered 8
03	1	Identify the part numbered 1
	2	Identify the part numbered 2
	3	Identify the part numbered 3
	4	Identify the part numbered 4
	5	Identify the part numbered 5
04	1	Identify the part numbered 1

	2	Identify the part numbered 2
	3	Identify the part numbered 3
	4	Identify the part numbered 4
	5	Identify the vertical ridge numbered 5
	6	Identify the part numbered 6
	7	Identify the part numbered 7
	8	Identify the concave depression numbered 8
	9	Identify the part numbered 9
05	1	Identify the part numbered 1
	2	Identify the part numbered 2
	3	Identify the part numbered 3
	4	Identify the part numbered 4
	5	Identify the holes numbered 5
06	1	Identify the part numbered 1
	2	Identify the part numbered 2
	3	Identify the part numbered 3
	4	Identify the part numbered 4
07	1	Identify the holes numbered 1
	2	Identify the part numbered 2
	3	Identify the part numbered 3
	4	Identify the smooth area numbered 4
	5	Identify the part numbered 5
	6	Identify the part numbered 6
08	1	Identify the part numbered 1
	2	Identify the part numbered 2
	3	Identify the part numbered 3
09	1	Identify the part numbered 1
	2	Identify the part numbered 2
	3	Identify the depression numbered 3
	4	Identify the part numbered 4
	5	Identify the part numbered 5
10	1	Identify the part numbered 1
	2	Identify the part numbered 2
11	1	identify right or left of this bone

PATELLA
Type **PATELLA** in white space in tool bar to bring up these images

Picture #	Question #	Question
01	1	Identify the part numbered 1
	2	Identify the part numbered 2
02	1	Identify the depression numbered 1
	2	Identify the depression numbered 2
	3	Identify the part numbered 3
	4	Identify the part numbered 4
03	1	Identify the part numbered 1
	2	Identify the part numbered 2
04	1	Identify the part numbered 1
	2	Identify the depression numbered 2
	3	Identify the depression numbered 3
	4	Identify the part numbered 4
05	1	Identify right or left of bone numbered 1

TIBIA
Type **TIBIA** in white space in tool bar to bring up these images

Picture #	Question #	Question
01	1	Identify the part numbered 1
	2	Identify the part numbered 2
	3	Identify the part numbered 3
02	1	Identify the part numbered 1
	2	Identify the part numbered 2
	3	Identify the part numbered 3
	4	Identify the part numbered 4
	5	Identify the depression numbered 5
03	1	Identify the part numbered 1
	2	Identify the part numbered 2
	3	What specific bone articulates to the concave area numbered 4
04	1	Identify the part numbered 1
	2	Identify the part numbered 2
	3	Identify the depression numbered 3
	4	Identify the specific bone and part that articulates to the area numbered 4
	5	Identify the depression numbered 5
	6	What specific bone articulates to the concave area numbered 6

	7	Identify the part numbered 7
05	1	Identify the part numbered 1
	2	Identify the part numbered 2
	3	Identify the rough raised area numbered 3
06	1	Identify the part numbered 1
	2	Identify the part numbered 2
	3	Identify the pointed structure numbered 3
	4	What bone and part articulates to the area numbered 4
07	1	Identify the part numbered 1
	2	Identify the depression numbered 2
	3	What bone articulates to the concave area numbered 3
08	1	Identify the depressions numbered 1
	2	Identify the pointed structure numbered 2
	3	Identify the structure numbered 3
09	1	Identify this bone
	2	Determine left or right for this bone

FIBULA
Type **FIBULA** in white space in tool bar to bring up these images

Picture #	Question #	Question
01	1	Identify the part numbered 1
	2	Identify the part numbered 2
02	1	Identify the part numbered 1
	2	Identify the part numbered 2
03	1	Identify the part numbered 1
	2	The part numbered 2 articulates to what bone?
04	1	The area numbered 1 articulates to what specific area on which bone?
05	1	Identify this bone

FOOT
Type **FOOT** in white space in tool bar to bring up these images

Picture #	Question #	Question
01	1	Identify the specific bone numbered 1
	2	Identify the specific bone numbered 2
	3	Identify the specific bone numbered 3
	4	Identify the specific bone numbered 4
	5	Identify the specific bone numbered 5

		6	Identify the specific bone numbered 6
		7	Identify the specific bone numbered 7
		8	Identify the specific bone numbered 8
02		1	Identify the specific bone numbered 1
		2	Identify the specific bone numbered 2
		3	Identify the specific bone numbered 3
		4	Identify the specific bone numbered 4
		5	Identify the specific bones numbered 5
		6	Identify the specific bone numbered 6
		7	Identify the specific part and bone numbered 7
		8	Identify the specific part and bone numbered 8
		9	Identify the specific part and bone numbered 9
		10	Identify the specific bone numbered 10
		11	Identify the specific bone numbered
		12	Identify the specific bone numbered
		13	Identify the specific part and bone numbered 13
		14	Identify the specific part and bone numbered 14
		15	Identify the specific part and bone numbered 15
03		1	Identify the bone numbered 1
		2	Identify the bone numbered 2
		3	Identify the part numbered 3
		4	Identify the part numbered 4
		5	Identify the bone numbered 5
04		1	Identify the part numbered 1
		2	Identify the bone numbered 2
		3	Identify the bone numbered 3
		4	Identify the bone numbered 4
		5	Identify the specific finger numbered 5
05		1	Identify the bone numbered 1
		2	Identify the bone numbered 2
		3	Identify the part numbered 3
		4	Identify the part numbered 4
		5	Identify the bone numbered 5
		6	Identify the bone numbered 6

BONE HISTOLOGY
Type **BONE HIST** in white space in tool bar to bring up these images

Picture #	Question #	Question
01	1	Identify the tissue numbered 1.
	2	Identify the structure numbered 2.
	3	Identify the entire structure colored light red and numbered 3.
02	1	Identify the part numbered 1.
	2	Identify the structure numbered 2.
	3	Identify the structure (the line) numbered 3.
03	1	Identify the structure numbered 1.

JOINTS (ARTICULATION)
Type **JOINT** in white space in tool bar to bring up these images

Picture #	Question #	Question
01	1	Identify the specific joint numbered 1
02	1	Identify the specific joint numbered 1
03	1	Identify the specific joint numbered 1
	2	Identify the specific joint numbered 2
04	1	Identify the depression numbered 1
	2	Identify the round process numbered 2
	3	Identify the process numbered 3
	4	Identify the spine numbered 4
	5	Identify the anatomical division numbered 5
	6	Identify the structure numbered 6
05	1	Identify the specific joint numbered 1
06	1	Identify the bone numbered 1
	2	Identify the process numbered 2
	3	Identify the bone numbered 3
	4	Identify the bone numbered 4
	5	Identify the process numbered 5
	6	Identify the concave depression numbered 6
07	1	Identify the specific joint numbered 1
08	1	Identify the surface numbered 1
	2	Identify the cartilage numbered 2
	3	Identify the process numbered 3
09	1	Identify the specific joint numbered 1
	2	Identify the specific joint numbered 2

10	1	Identify the specific joint numbered 1
11	1	Identify the specific joint numbered 1
12	1	Identify the specific joint numbered 1
13	1	Identify the specific joint numbered 1
14	1	Identify the specific joint numbered 1
15	1	Identify the specific joint numbered 1
16	1	Identify the bone numbered 1
	2	Identify the bone numbered 2
	3	Identify the fossa numbered 3
	4	Identify the fossa numbered 4
	5	Identify the process numbered 5
	6	Identify the process numbered 6
	7	Identify the specific joint numbered 7
17	1	Identify the specific joint numbered 1
18	1	Identify the specific joint numbered 1
19	1	Identify the specific joint numbered 1
	2	Identify the specific joint numbered 2
20	1	Identify the specific joint numbered 1
21	1	Identify the depression numbered 1
	2	Identify the process numbered 2
	3	Identify the hole numbered 3
	4	Identify the specific joint numbered 4 (light green in color)
22	1	Identify the specific joint numbered 1
23	1	Identify the process numbered 1
	2	Identify the process numbered 2
	3	Identify the process numbered 3
	4	Identify the process numbered 4
	5	Identify the fossa numbered 5
	6	Identify the process numbered 6
	7	Identify the fossa numbered 7
24	1	Identify the specific joint numbered 1
25	1	Identify the process numbered 1
	2	Identify the process numbered 2
	3	Identify the process numbered 3
	4	Identify the depression numbered 4
	5	Identify the depression numbered 5
	6	Identify the process numbered 6
	7	Identify the specific joint numbered 7

26	1	Identify the specific joint numbered 1
27	1	Identify the process numbered 1
	2	Identify the depression numbered 2
	3	Identify the process numbered 3
	4	Identify the process numbered 4
	5	Identify the bone numbered 5
	6	Identify the bone numbered 6
28	1	Identify the specific joint numbered 1
	2	Identify the specific joint numbered 2
29	1	Identify the bone numbered 1
	2	Identify the process numbered 2
	3	Identify the process numbered 3
	4	Identify the depression numbered 4
30	1	Identify the specific joint numbered 1
31	1	Identify the spine numbered 1
	2	Identify the spine numbered 2
	3	Identify the spine numbered 3
	4	Identify the spine numbered 4
	5	Identify the concave area numbered 5
	6	Identify the round process numbered 6
	7	Identify the concave structure numbered 7
	8	Identify the process numbered 8
32	1	Identify the specific joint numbered 1
	2	Identify the specific joint numbered 2

HUMAN SKELETAL MUSCLES
Type **MUSCLEPICT** in white space in tool bar to bring up these images

Picture #	Question #	Question
01	1	Identify the human skeletal muscle numbered 1
	2	Identify the human skeletal muscle numbered 2
	3	Identify the human skeletal muscle numbered 3
02	1	Identify the human skeletal muscle numbered 1
03	1	Identify the human skeletal muscle numbered 1
04	1	Identify the human skeletal muscle numbered 1
	2	Identify the human skeletal muscle numbered 2
	3	Identify the human skeletal muscle numbered 3
	4	Identify the human skeletal muscle numbered 4

	5	Identify the human skeletal muscle numbered 5
05	1	Identify the human skeletal muscle numbered 1
	2	Identify the human skeletal muscle numbered 2
	3	Identify the human skeletal muscle numbered 3
	4	Identify the human skeletal muscle numbered 4
	5	Identify the deep human skeletal muscle numbered 5
06	1	Identify the human skeletal muscle numbered 1
	2	Identify the human skeletal muscle numbered 2
	3	Identify the human skeletal muscle numbered 3
	4	Identify the human skeletal muscle numbered 4
	5	Identify the human skeletal muscle numbered 5
07	1	Identify the human skeletal muscle numbered 1
	2	Identify the human skeletal muscle numbered 2
	3	Identify the human skeletal muscle numbered 3
	4	Identify the human skeletal muscle numbered 4
	5	Identify the human skeletal muscle numbered 5
	6	Identify the human skeletal muscle numbered 6
	7	Identify the human skeletal muscle numbered 7
	8	Identify the human skeletal muscle numbered 8
	9	Identify the human skeletal muscle numbered 9
08	1	Identify the human skeletal muscle numbered 1
	2	Identify the human skeletal muscle numbered 2
	3	Identify the human skeletal muscle numbered 3
	4	Identify the human skeletal muscle numbered 4
	5	Identify the human skeletal muscle numbered 5
	6	Identify the human skeletal muscle numbered 6
	7	Identify the human skeletal muscle numbered 7
	8	Identify the human skeletal muscle (outer most) layer numbered 7
09	1	Identify the human skeletal muscle numbered 1
	2	Identify the human skeletal muscle numbered 2
	3	Identify the human skeletal muscle numbered 3
	4	Identify the superficial human skeletal muscle numbered 4
	5	Identify the human skeletal muscle numbered 5
	6	Identify the human skeletal muscle numbered 6
10	1	Identify the human skeletal muscle numbered 1
	2	Identify the human skeletal muscle numbered 2
	3	Identify the human skeletal muscle numbered 3
	4	Identify the human skeletal muscle numbered 4

	5	Identify the human skeletal muscle numbered 5
	6	Identify the superficial human skeletal muscle numbered 6
	7	Identify the human skeletal muscle numbered 7
	8	Identify the human skeletal muscle numbered 8
	9	Identify the human skeletal muscle numbered 9
11	1	Identify the human skeletal muscle numbered 1
	2	Identify the human skeletal muscle numbered 2
	3	Identify the human skeletal muscle numbered 3
	4	Identify the human skeletal muscle numbered 4
	5	Identify the human skeletal muscle numbered 5
	6	Identify the human skeletal muscle numbered 6
12	1	Identify the human skeletal muscle numbered 1
	2	Identify the human skeletal muscle numbered 2
	3	Identify the human skeletal muscle numbered 3
13	1	Identify the human skeletal muscle numbered 4
	2	Identify the human skeletal muscle numbered 2
	3	Identify the external human skeletal muscle numbered 3
	4	Identify the human skeletal muscle numbered 4
14	1	Identify the human skeletal muscle numbered 1
	2	Identify the human skeletal muscle numbered 2
	3	Identify the human skeletal muscle numbered 3
	4	Identify the human skeletal muscle numbered 4
	5	Identify the human skeletal muscle numbered 5
	6	Identify the human skeletal muscle numbered 6
15	1	Identify the human skeletal muscle numbered 1
	2	Identify the human skeletal muscle numbered 2
	3	Identify the human skeletal muscle numbered 3
	4	Identify the human skeletal muscle numbered 4
	5	Identify the human skeletal muscle numbered 5
	6	Identify the human skeletal muscle numbered 6
	7	Identify the human skeletal muscle numbered 7
	8	Identify the human skeletal muscle numbered 8
	9	Identify the human skeletal muscle numbered 9
16	1	Identify the deep human skeletal muscle numbered 1
	2	Identify the deep human skeletal muscle numbered 2
	3	Identify the deep human skeletal muscle numbered 3
17	1	Identify the human skeletal muscle numbered 1
	2	Identify the human skeletal muscle numbered 2

	3	Identify the human skeletal muscle numbered 3
	4	Identify the human skeletal muscle numbered 4
	5	Identify the human skeletal muscle numbered 5
	6	Identify the human skeletal muscle numbered 6
18	1	Identify the human skeletal muscle numbered 1
	2	Identify the human skeletal muscle numbered 2
19	1	Identify the human skeletal muscle numbered 1
	2	Identify the deep human skeletal muscle numbered 2
	3	Identify the human skeletal muscle numbered 3
	4	Identify the human skeletal muscle numbered 4
	5	Identify the human skeletal muscle numbered 5
	6	Identify the human skeletal muscle numbered 6
	7	Identify the human skeletal muscle numbered 7
	8	Identify the human skeletal muscle numbered 8
	9	Identify the human skeletal muscle numbered 9
20	1	Identify the human skeletal muscle numbered 1
	2	Identify the human skeletal muscle numbered 2
21	1	Identify the human skeletal muscle numbered 1
22	1	Identify the human skeletal muscle numbered 1
	2	Identify the human skeletal muscle numbered 2
	3	Identify the human skeletal muscle numbered 3
	4	Identify the human skeletal muscle numbered 4
	5	Identify the human skeletal muscle numbered 5
	6	Identify the human skeletal muscle numbered 6
	7	Identify the human skeletal muscle numbered 7
	8	Identify the human skeletal muscle numbered 8
23	1	Identify the human skeletal muscle numbered 1
	2	Identify the human skeletal muscle numbered 2
	3	Identify the human skeletal muscle numbered 3
	4	Identify the human skeletal muscle numbered 4
	5	Identify the human skeletal muscle numbered 5
24	1	Identify the human skeletal muscle numbered 1
25	1	Identify the human skeletal muscle numbered 1
26	1	Identify the human skeletal muscle numbered 1
27	1	Identify the human skeletal muscle numbered 1
28	1	Identify the human skeletal muscle numbered 1
	2	Identify the human skeletal muscle numbered 2
	3	Identify the human skeletal muscle numbered 3

	4	Identify the human skeletal muscle numbered 4
29	1	Identify the human skeletal muscle numbered 1
	2	Identify the human skeletal muscle numbered 2
	3	Identify the human skeletal muscle numbered 3
	4	Identify the human skeletal muscle numbered 4
	5	Identify the human skeletal muscle numbered 5
	6	Identify the human skeletal muscle numbered 6
	7	Identify the human skeletal muscle numbered 7
	8	Identify the human skeletal muscle numbered 8
	9	Identify the deep human skeletal muscle located between the ribs numbered 9
30	1	Identify the human skeletal muscle numbered 1
	2	Identify the human skeletal muscle numbered 2
	3	Identify the human skeletal muscle numbered 3
	4	Identify the human skeletal muscle numbered 4
31	1	Identify the human skeletal muscle numbered 1
	2	Identify the human skeletal muscle numbered 2
	3	Identify the human skeletal muscle numbered 3
	4	Identify the human skeletal muscle numbered 4
	5	Identify the human skeletal muscle numbered 5
	6	Identify the deep human skeletal muscle numbered 6
	7	Identify the human skeletal muscle numbered 7
32	1	Identify the human skeletal muscle numbered 1
	2	Identify the human skeletal muscle numbered 2
	3	Identify the human skeletal muscle numbered 3
	4	Identify the human skeletal muscle numbered 4
	5	Identify the deep human skeletal muscle numbered 5
	6	Identify the deep human skeletal muscle numbered 6
33	1	Identify the human skeletal muscle numbered 1
	2	Identify the human skeletal muscle numbered 2
	3	Identify the human skeletal muscle numbered 3
	4	Identify the human skeletal muscle numbered 4
	5	Identify the human skeletal muscle numbered 5
34	1	Identify the human skeletal muscle numbered 1
	2	Identify the human skeletal muscle numbered 2
	3	Identify the human skeletal muscle numbered 3
	4	Identify the human skeletal muscle numbered 4
	5	Identify the human skeletal muscle numbered 5
35	1	Identify the human skeletal muscle numbered 1

	2	Identify the human skeletal muscle numbered 2
	3	Identify the human skeletal muscle numbered 3
	4	Identify the human skeletal muscle numbered 4
	5	Identify the human skeletal muscle numbered 5
	6	Identify the human skeletal muscle numbered 6
36	1	Identify the human skeletal muscle numbered 1
	2	Identify the human skeletal muscle numbered 2
37	1	Identify the human skeletal muscle numbered 1
	2	Identify the deep human skeletal muscle numbered 2
	3	Identify the human skeletal muscle numbered 3
	4	Identify the human skeletal muscle numbered 4
	(BLACK) 5	Identify the deep human skeletal muscle numbered (BLACK) 5.
	(RED) 5	Identify the human leg skeletal muscle numbered (RED) 5.
38	1	Identify the human skeletal muscle numbered 1
	2	Identify the human skeletal muscle numbered 2
	3	Identify the human skeletal muscle numbered 3
	4	Identify the human skeletal muscle numbered 4
	5	Identify the human skeletal muscle numbered 5
	6	Identify the human skeletal muscle numbered 6
	7	Identify the human skeletal muscle numbered 7
39	1	Identify the human skeletal muscle numbered 1
40	1	Identify the human skeletal muscle numbered1
	2	Identify the human skeletal muscle numbered 2
	3	Identify the human skeletal muscle numbered 3
	4	Identify the human skeletal muscle numbered 4
	5	Identify the human skeletal muscle numbered 5
	6	Identify the human skeletal muscle numbered 6
	7	Identify the human skeletal muscle numbered 7
	8	Identify the human skeletal muscle numbered 8
41	1	Identify the human skeletal muscle numbered 1
	2	Identify the human skeletal muscle numbered 2
	3	Identify the human skeletal muscle numbered 3
	4	Identify the human skeletal muscle numbered 4
	5	Identify the human skeletal muscle numbered 5
	6	Identify the human skeletal muscle numbered 6
42	1	Identify the human skeletal muscle numbered 1
	2	Identify the deep human skeletal muscle numbered 2
	3	Identify the human skeletal muscle numbered 3

	4	Identify the human skeletal muscle numbered 4
	5	Identify the human skeletal muscle numbered 5
	6	Identify the human skeletal muscle numbered 6
	7	Identify the human skeletal muscle numbered 7
	8	Identify the human skeletal muscle numbered 8
	9	Identify the human skeletal muscle numbered 9.
43	1	Identify the human skeletal muscle numbered 1
	2	Identify the human skeletal muscle numbered 2
	3	Identify the human skeletal muscle numbered 3
	4	Identify the human skeletal muscle numbered 4
	5	Identify the human skeletal muscle numbered 5
	6	Identify the human skeletal muscle numbered 6
	7	Identify the human skeletal muscle numbered 7
	8	Identify the human skeletal muscle numbered 8
	9	Identify the human skeletal muscle numbered 9
	10	Identify the human skeletal muscle numbered 10
	11	Identify the human skeletal muscle numbered 11
	12	Identify the human skeletal muscle numbered 12
	13	Identify the deep human skeletal muscle numbered 13
	14	Identify the deep human skeletal muscle numbered 14
44	1	Identify the human skeletal muscle numbered 1
	2	Identify the human skeletal muscle numbered 2
	3	Identify the human skeletal muscle numbered 3
	4	Identify the human skeletal muscle numbered 4
	5	Identify the human skeletal muscle numbered 5
	6	Identify the human skeletal muscle numbered 6
	7	Identify the human skeletal muscle numbered 7
	8	Identify the human skeletal muscle numbered 8
45	1	Identify the human skeletal muscle numbered 1
	2	Identify the human skeletal muscle numbered 2
46	1	Identify the human skeletal muscle numbered 1
	2	Identify the human skeletal muscle numbered 2
	3	Identify the human skeletal muscle numbered 3
	4	Identify the human skeletal muscle numbered 4
	5	Identify the human skeletal muscle numbered 5
47	1	Identify the human skeletal muscle numbered 1
	2	Identify the human skeletal muscle numbered 2
	3	Identify the human skeletal muscle numbered 3

	4	Identify the human skeletal muscle numbered 4
	5	Identify the human skeletal muscle numbered 5
	6	Identify the human skeletal muscle numbered 6
	7	Identify the human skeletal muscle numbered 7
	8	Identify the human skeletal muscle numbered 8

HUMAN SKELETAL MUSCLES
(PLASTIC MODELS)
Type **HUMANPLASTIC** in white space in tool bar to bring up these images

Picture #	Question #	Question
01	1	Identify the human skeletal muscle on the plastic model numbered 1
	2	Identify the human skeletal muscle on the plastic model numbered 2
	3	Identify the human skeletal muscle on the plastic model numbered 3
	4	Identify the deep human skeletal muscle on the plastic model numbered 4
	5	Identify the human skeletal muscle on the plastic model numbered 5
	6	Identify the deep human skeletal muscle on the plastic model numbered 6
02	1	Identify the human skeletal muscle on the plastic model numbered 1
	2	Identify the human skeletal muscle on the plastic model numbered 2
	3	Identify the human skeletal muscle on the plastic model numbered 3
	4	Identify the human skeletal muscle on the plastic model numbered 4
	5	Identify the human skeletal muscle on the plastic model numbered 5
	6	Identify the human skeletal muscle on the plastic model numbered 6.
	7	Identify the human skeletal muscle on the plastic model numbered 7
03	1	Identify the human skeletal muscle on the plastic model numbered 1
	2	Identify the deep human skeletal muscle on the plastic model numbered 2
	3	Identify the deep human skeletal muscle on the plastic model numbered 3.
04	1	Identify the human skeletal muscle on the plastic model numbered 1
	2	Identify the human skeletal muscle on the plastic model numbered 2.
	3	Identify the human skeletal muscle on the plastic model numbered 3
	4	Identify the deep human skeletal muscle on the plastic model numbered 4.
	5	Identify the deep human skeletal muscle on the plastic model numbered 5.
05	1	Identify the human skeletal muscle on the plastic model numbered 1.
	2	Identify the human skeletal muscle on the plastic model numbered 2.
	3	Identify the human skeletal muscle on the plastic model numbered 3.
	4	Identify the human skeletal muscle on the plastic model numbered 4.
06	1	Identify the human skeletal muscle on the plastic model numbered 1
	2	Identify the human skeletal muscle on the plastic model numbered 2
	3	Identify the human skeletal muscle on the plastic model numbered 3

	4	Identify the human skeletal muscle on the plastic model numbered 4
	5	Identify the human skeletal muscle on the plastic model numbered 5.
	6	Identify the human skeletal muscle on the plastic model numbered 6.
07	1	Identify the human skeletal muscle on the plastic leg model numbered 1.
	2	Identify the human skeletal muscle on the plastic leg model numbered 2.
	3	Identify the human skeletal muscle on the plastic leg model numbered 3.
	4	Identify the human skeletal muscle on the plastic leg model numbered 4.
	5	Identify the human skeletal muscle on the plastic leg model numbered 5.
	6	Identify the gray structure on the human leg numbered 6.
08	1	Identify the human skeletal muscle on the plastic leg model numbered 1.
	2	Identify the human skeletal muscle on the plastic leg model numbered 2.
	3	Identify the human skeletal muscle on the plastic leg model numbered 3.
	4	Identify the human skeletal muscle on the plastic leg model numbered 4.
	5	Identify the human skeletal muscle on the plastic leg model numbered 5.
	6	Identify the human skeletal muscle on the plastic leg model numbered 6.
	7	Identify the human skeletal muscle on the plastic leg model numbered 7.
	8	Identify the gray tendon structure on the plastic leg model numbered 8.
	9	Identify the gray tendon structure on the plastic leg model numbered 9.
09	1	Identify the human skeletal muscle on the plastic leg model numbered 1.
	2	Identify the human skeletal muscle on the plastic leg model numbered 2.
	3	Identify the human skeletal muscle on the plastic leg model numbered 3.
	4	Identify the human skeletal muscle on the plastic leg model numbered 4.
	5	Identify the human skeletal muscle on the plastic leg model numbered 5.
	6	Identify the human skeletal muscle on the plastic leg model numbered 6.
10	1	Identify the human skeletal muscle on the plastic leg model numbered 1
	2	Identify the human skeletal muscle on the plastic leg model numbered 2.
	3	Identify the human skeletal muscle on the plastic leg model numbered 3
	4	Identify the human skeletal muscle on the plastic leg model numbered 4.
	5	Identify the human skeletal muscle on the plastic leg model numbered 5.
	6	Identify the human skeletal muscle on the plastic leg model numbered 6.
	7	Identify the human skeletal muscle on the plastic leg model numbered 7.
11	1	Identify the human skeletal muscle on the plastic leg model numbered 1.
	2	Identify the human skeletal muscle on the plastic leg model numbered 2.
	3	Identify the human skeletal muscle on the plastic leg model numbered 3.
	4	Identify the human skeletal muscle on the plastic leg model numbered 4.
	5	Identify the human skeletal muscle on the plastic leg model numbered 5.
	6	Identify the human skeletal muscle on the plastic leg model numbered 6.
	7	Identify the human skeletal muscle on the plastic leg model numbered 7.

	8	Identify the human skeletal muscle on the plastic leg model numbered 8.
12	1	Identify the human skeletal muscle on the plastic head model numbered 1
	2	Identify the human skeletal muscle on the plastic head model numbered 2.
	3	Identify the human skeletal muscle on the plastic head model numbered 3.
	4	Identify the human skeletal muscle on the plastic head model numbered 4.
	5	Identify the human skeletal muscle on the plastic head model numbered 5.
	6	Identify the human skeletal muscle on the plastic head model numbered 6.
	7	Identify the human skeletal muscle on the plastic head model numbered 7.
	8	Identify the human skeletal muscle on the plastic head model numbered 8.
	9	Identify the human skeletal muscle on the plastic head model numbered 9.
13	1	Identify the human skeletal muscle on the plastic leg model numbered 1.
	2	Identify the human skeletal muscle on the plastic leg model numbered 2.
	3	Identify the human skeletal muscle on the plastic leg model numbered 3.
	4	Identify the human skeletal muscle on the plastic leg model numbered 4.
	5	Identify the human skeletal muscle on the plastic leg model numbered 5.
	6	Identify the human skeletal muscle on the plastic leg model numbered 6.
	7	Identify the human skeletal muscle on the plastic leg model numbered 7.
14	1	Identify the human skeletal muscle on the plastic head model numbered 1.
	2	Identify the human skeletal muscle on the plastic head model numbered 2.
	3	Identify the human skeletal muscle on the plastic head model numbered 3.
	4	Identify the human skeletal muscle on the plastic head model numbered 4.
15	1	Identify the human skeletal muscle on the plastic leg model numbered 1.
	2	Identify the deep human skeletal muscle on the plastic leg model numbered 2.
	3	Identify the human skeletal muscle on the plastic leg model numbered 3.
	4	Identify the human skeletal muscle on the plastic leg model numbered 4.
	5	Identify the human skeletal muscle on the plastic leg model numbered 5.
	6	Identify the human skeletal muscle on the plastic leg model numbered 6.
	7	Identify the human skeletal muscle on the plastic leg model numbered 7.
	8	Identify the human skeletal muscle on the plastic leg model numbered 8.
	9	Identify the human skeletal muscle on the plastic leg model numbered 9.
16	1	Identify the human skeletal muscle on the plastic head model numbered 1.
	2	Identify the human skeletal muscle on the plastic head model numbered 2.
	3	Identify the human skeletal muscle on the plastic head model numbered 3.
	4	Identify the human skeletal muscle on the plastic head model numbered 4.
	5	Identify the human skeletal muscle on the plastic head model numbered 5.
	6	Identify the white structure on the human plastic head numbered 6.
17	1	Identify the human skeletal muscle on the plastic head model numbered 1.
	2	Identify the human skeletal muscle on the plastic head model numbered 2.

	3	Identify the human skeletal muscle on the plastic head model numbered 3.
18	1	Identify the human skeletal muscle on the plastic torso model numbered 1.
	2	Identify the human skeletal muscle on the plastic torso model numbered 2.
	3	Identify the human skeletal muscle on the plastic torso model numbered 3.
	4	Identify the human skeletal muscle on the plastic torso model numbered 4.
	5	Identify the human skeletal muscle on the plastic torso model numbered 5.
	6	Identify the deep human skeletal muscle on the plastic torso model numbered 6.
	7	Identify the human skeletal muscle on the plastic torso model numbered 7
	8	Identify the human skeletal muscle on the plastic torso model numbered 8.
	9	Identify the nerve on the plastic torso numbered 9.
19	1	Identify the human skeletal muscle on the plastic torso model numbered 1.
	2	Identify the human skeletal muscle on the plastic torso model numbered 2.
	3	Identify the human skeletal muscle on the plastic torso model numbered 3.
	4	Identify the human skeletal muscle on the plastic torso model numbered 4.
	5	Identify the human skeletal muscle on the plastic torso model numbered 5.
20	1	Identify the human skeletal muscle on the plastic torso model numbered 1.
	2	Identify the human skeletal muscle on the plastic torso model numbered 2.
	3	Identify the human skeletal muscle on the plastic torso model numbered 3.
	4	Identify the process and bone on the plastic torso numbered 4.
	5	Identify the process and bone on the plastic torso numbered 5.
	6	Identify the bone on the plastic torso numbered 6.
21	1	Identify the human skeletal muscle on the plastic torso model numbered 1.
	2	Identify the human skeletal muscle on the plastic torso model numbered 2.
	3	Identify the human skeletal muscle on the plastic torso model numbered 3.
	4	Identify the human skeletal muscle on the plastic torso model numbered 4.
	5	Identify the human skeletal muscle on the plastic torso model numbered 5.
22	1	Identify the human skeletal muscle on the plastic torso model numbered 1.
	2	Identify the deep human skeletal muscle on the plastic torso model numbered 2.
	3	Identify the human skeletal muscle on the plastic torso model numbered 3.
	4	Identify the nerve on the plastic torso model numbered 4.
23	1	Identify the specific bone on the plastic arm model numbered 1.
	2	Identify the specific skeletal muscle on the plastic arm model numbered 2.
	3	Identify the specific skeletal muscle on the plastic arm model numbered 3.
	4	Identify the specific skeletal muscle on the plastic arm model numbered 4.
	5	Identify the specific skeletal muscle on the plastic arm model numbered 5.
	6	Identify the specific skeletal muscle on the plastic arm model numbered 6.
	7	Identify the specific skeletal muscle on the plastic arm model numbered 7.
	8	Identify the specific skeletal muscle on the plastic arm model numbered 8.

	9	Identify the specific skeletal muscle on the plastic arm model numbered 9.
	10	Identify the specific skeletal muscle on the plastic arm model numbered 10.
	11	Identify the specific skeletal muscle on the plastic arm model numbered 11.
	12	Identify the specific skeletal muscle on the plastic arm model numbered 12.
	13	Identify the specific whitish structure on the plastic arm model numbered 13.
24	I	Identify the specific skeletal muscle on the plastic arm model numbered 1.
	2	Identify the specific skeletal muscle on the plastic arm model numbered 2.
	3	Identify the specific skeletal muscle on the plastic arm model numbered 3.
	3A	Identify the specific skeletal muscle head on the plastic arm model numbered 3A.
	3B	Identify the specific skeletal muscle head on the plastic arm model numbered 3B.
	4	Identify the specific skeletal muscle on the plastic arm model numbered 4.
	5	Identify the specific skeletal muscle on the plastic arm model numbered 5.
	6	Identify the specific skeletal muscle on the plastic arm model numbered 6.
	7	Identify the specific peripheral nerve (yellow in color) on the plastic arm model numbered 7.
25	1	Identify the specific skeletal muscle on the plastic arm model numbered 1.
	2	Identify the specific skeletal muscle on the plastic arm model numbered 2.
	3	Identify the specific skeletal muscle on the plastic arm model numbered 3.
	4	Identify the specific skeletal muscle on the plastic arm model numbered 4.
	5	Identify the specific skeletal muscle on the plastic arm model numbered 5.
	6	Identify the specific skeletal muscle on the plastic arm model numbered 6.
	7	Identify the specific skeletal muscle on the plastic arm model numbered 7.
	8	Identify the specific skeletal muscle on the plastic arm model numbered 8.

Type **MUSCLEHIST** in white space in tool bar to bring up these images

Picture #	Question #	Question
01	1	Identify the oval structure numbered 1.
	2	Identify the specific connective membrane numbered 2.
	3	Identify the specific connective membrane numbered 3.
02	1	Identify the specific tissue lettered "A".
03	1	Identify the specific structure numbered 1.
04	1	Identify the specific tissue lettered "B".
05	1	Identify the specific tissue numbered "C".
	2	Identify the structure numbered 2.
06	1	Identify the specific tissue lettered "D"
	2	Identify the specific structure (line) numbered 2.
07	1	Identify the specific tissue lettered "E".
	2	Identify the specific structure numbered 2.

NERVOUS SYSTEM
(NERVE CELLS/NEUON)
Type **NEURON** in white space in tool bar to bring up these images

Picture #	Question #	Question
01	1	Identify the large part of the cell model that is light red in color an numbered 1
	2	Identify the projections on the cell model numbered 2.
	3	Identify the projection on the cell model numbered 3.
02	1	Identify the projections on the cell model numbered 1.
	2	Identify the structure on the cell model numbered 2.
	3	Identify the structure on the cell model numbered 3.
	4	Identify the structures on the cell model numbered 4.
	5	Identify the yellow structure on the cell model numbered 5.
03	1	Identify the part on the cell model numbered 1
	2	Identify the yellow structure on the cell model numbered 2.
	3	Identify the gray layer on the cell model numbered 3.
	4	Identify the blue structures on the cell model numbered 4.
	5	Identify the area on the cell model numbered 5
	6	Identify the structure (brown lines) on the cell model numbered 6.
04	1	Identify the projection on the cell model numbered 1
	2	Identify the bump structures on the cell model numbered 2.
	3	Identify the string like structure on the cell model numbered 3.

	4	Identify the area on the cell model numbered 4
	5	Identify the round organelle on the cell model numbered 6.
	6	Identify the dark lines on the cell model numbered 6
05	1	Identify the yellow substance on the cell model numbered 1.
	2	Identify the reddish structure on the cell model numbered 2.
	3	Identify the grayish structure on the cell model numbered 3.
	4	Identify the pinkish structure on the cell model numbered 4.
	5	Identify the dark bump on the cell model numbered 5
	6	Identify the area on the cell model numbered 6
06	1	Identify the structure on the cell model numbered 1
	2	Identify the yellow structure on the cell model numbered 2.
	3	Identify the structure on the cell model numbered 3.
	4	Identify the structure on the cell model numbered 4.
07	1	Identify the structure on the cell model numbered 1
	2	Identify the structures on the cell model numbered 2.
	3	Identify the structure on the cell model numbered 3.
	4	Identify the structure on the cell model numbered 4.
	5	Identify the round structure on the cell model numbered 5.
	6	Identify the blue structures on the cell model numbered 6
	7	Identify the structure on the cell model numbered 7
08	1	Identify the structure on the cell model numbered 1
	2	Identify the layer on the cell model numbered 2.
	3	Identify the structure on the cell model numbered 3.
	4	Identify the indentation on the cell model numbered 4.
	5	Identify the gray structure on the cell model numbered 5
	6	Identify the layer on the cell model numbered 6.
09	1	Identify the structure on the cell model numbered1
	2	Identify the structure on the cell model numbered 2
	3	Identify the structures on the cell model numbered 3.
10	1	Identify the projection on the cell model numbered 1.
	2	Identify the projection on the cell model numbered 2.
	3	Identify the structure in the picture numbered 3.
	4	The neuron lettered "A" conducting the impulse toward structure number 3 is called the:
	5	The neuron lettered "B" conducting the impulse away from the structure numbered 3 is called the:
11	1	Which structure on the neuron is composed of rough endoplasmic reticulum and is a site for protein synthesis (A, B, C, D, E, F,G)?
	2	Which structure on the neuron is an afferent projection (A, B, C, D, E, F,G)?
	3	Which structure on the neuron contains the neurotransmitter acetylcholine (A, B, C, D, E, F,G)?

	4	Which structure on the neuron is almost always required for nerve regeneration (A, B, C, D, E, F,G)?
	5	Which structure on the neuron is an efferent projection (A, B, C, D, E, F,G)?
	6	Which structure on the neuron is a lipid-protein covering that prevents sodium channel from opening and affects nerve impulse velocity (A, B, C, D, E, F,G)?
	7	Which structure on the neuron is the trigger zone for nerve impulse on axon (A, B, C, D, E, F,G)?
	8	The neuron in the picture is classified as a (unipolar, bipolar, multipolar) neuron.
12	1	Identify the entire blue structure on the neuron model numbered 1.
	2	Identify the oval structure on the neuron model numbered 2.
	3	Identify the structure on the neuron model numbered 3.
	4	Identify the structure on the neuron model numbered 4.
	5	Identify the indentation on the neuron model numbered 5
	6	Identify the oval structure on the neuron model numbered 6.
	7	Identify the structure on the neuron model numbered 7.
	8	Identify the structure (gray mass) on the neuron model numbered 8.
	9	Identify the blue structure on the neuron model numbered 9.
	10	Identify the entire red structure on the neuron model numbered 10.
13	1	Identify the cone-shaped area were the nerve impulse arise (trigger zone) on the neuron model number 1.
	2	Identify the projection on the neuron model numbered 2.
	3	Identify the bulb-shaped structure on the neuron model numbered 3.
	4	Identify the structure on the neuron model numbered 4.
	5	Identify the projection (blue) on the neuron model numbered 5.
	6	Identify the specific portion (brown(on the neuron model numbered 6.
	7	Identify the layers (yellow) on the neuron model numbered 7.
	8	Identify the layers (yellow) on the neuron model numbered 8.
	9	Identify the intervals on the neuron model numbered 9.
	10	Identify the layer on the neuron model numbered 10.
14	1	Identify the organelle on the neuron model numbered 1.
	2	Identify the organelle (blue) on the neuron model numbered 2.
	3	Identify the organelle (green) on the neuron model numbered 3
	4	Identify the organelle (orange) on the neuron model numbered 4.
	5	Identify the organelle (brown) on the neuron model numbered 5.
	6	Identify the organelle (yellow) on the neuron model numbered 6.
	7	Identify the organelle (brown) on the neuron model numbered 7.
	8	Identify the organelle (brown with colored dots) on the neuron model numbered 8.
	9	Identify the filament structure on the neuron model numbered 9.
	10	Identify the projection on the neuron model numbered 10.
	11	Identify the bulb-shaped structure on the neuron model numbered 11.
	12	Identify the structure on the neuron model numbered 12.

15	1	Identify the small round yellow structures on the neuron model numbered 1
	2	Identify the type of cell on the neuron model numbered 2
	3	Identify the structure (yellow) on the neuron model numbered 3
	4	Identify the thin structures (gray) on the neuron model numbered 4
16	1	Identify the round red structures on the neuron model numbered 1
	2	Identify the long thin red structures on the neuron model numbered 2
	3	Identify the region on the neuron model numbered 3
	4	Identify the structures on the neuron model numbered 4
17	1	Identify the organelle of the cell on the neuron model numbered 1
	2	Identify the turquoise layer on the neuron model numbered 2
	3	Identify the small round yellow structures on the neuron model numbered 3

SHEEP BRAIN DISSECTIONS
Type **SHEEPBRAIN** in white space in tool bar to bring up these images

Picture #	Question #	Question
01	1	Identify the meninx numbered 1.
	2	Identify the bump on the sheep brain numbered 2.
02	1	Identify the lobe numbered 1.
	2	Identify the lobe numbered 2.
	3	Identify the lobe numbered 3.
	4	Identify the white structure numbered 4.
	5	Identify the white structure numbered 5.
	6	Identify the structure on the sheep brain numbered 6.
	7	Identify the structure on the sheep brain numbered 7.
	8	Identify the structure on the sheep brain numbered 8.
	9	Identify the structure on the sheep brain numbered 9.
03	1	Identify the lobe numbered 1.
	2	Identify the lobe numbered 2.
	3	Identify the structure numbered 3.
	4	Identify the lobe numbered 4.
	5	Identify the long slit numbered 5.
	6	Identify the deep groove numbered 6
	7	Identify the structure numbered 7.
04	1	Identify the long groove numbered 1.
	2	Identify the elevation numbered 2.
	3	Identify the small groove numbered 3.

05	1	Identify the oval structures numbered 1.
	2	Identify the lobe numbered 2.
06	1	Identify the thin nervous tissue membrane on the sheep brain numbered 1.
	2	Identify the structure on the sheep brain numbered 2.
	3	Identify the structure on the sheep brain numbered 3.
	4	Identify the structure on the sheep brain numbered 4.
	5	Identify the structure on the sheep brain numbered 5.
	6	Identify the structure on the sheep brain numbered 6.
	7	Identify the white structure on the sheep brain numbered 7.
	8	Identify the structure on the sheep brain numbered 8.
	9	Identify the structure on the sheep brain numbered 9.
07	1	Identify the lobe numbered 1.
	2	Identify the lobe numbered 2.
	3	Identify the lobe numbered 3.
	4	Identify the structure numbered 4.
	5	Identify the structure on the sheep brain numbered 5.
	6	Identify the structure on the sheep brain numbered 6.
	7	Identify the structure on the sheep brain numbered 7.
	8	Identify the structure on the sheep brain numbered 8.
	9	Identify the structure on the sheep brain numbered 9.
	10	Identify the groove on the sheep brain numbered 10.
	11	Identify the groove on the sheep brain numbered 11.
	12	Identify the groove on the sheep brain numbered 12.
08	1	Identify the structure on the sheep brain numbered 1.
	2	Identify the structure on the sheep brain numbered 2.
	3	Identify the structure on the sheep brain numbered 3.
09	1	Identify the white structure on the sheep brain numbered 1.
	2	Identify the white structure on the sheep brain numbered 2.
	3	Identify the structure on the sheep brain numbered 3.
	4	Identify the structure on the sheep brain numbered 4.
	5	Identify the structure on the sheep brain numbered 5.
	6	Identify the structure on the sheep brain numbered 6.
	7	Identify the structure on the sheep brain numbered 7.
	8	Identify the structure on the sheep brain numbered 8.
	9	Identify the structure on the sheep brain numbered 9.
	10	Identify the structure on the sheep brain numbered 10.
	11	Identify the structure on the sheep brain numbered 11.
	12	Identify the structure on the sheep brain numbered 12.

	13	Identify the structure on the sheep brain numbered 13.
	14	Identify the structure (open area) on the sheep brain numbered 14.
10	1	Identify the structure on the sheep brain numbered 1.
	2	Identify the structure on the sheep brain numbered 2.
	3	Identify the structure on the sheep brain numbered 3.
	4	Identify the groove on the sheep brain numbered 4.
	5	Identify the elevation on the sheep brain numbered 5.
11	1	Identify the structure on the sheep brain numbered 1.
	2	Identify the structure on the sheep brain numbered 2.
	3	Identify the ventricle numbered 3.
12	1	Identify the structure on the sheep brain numbered 1.
	2	Identify the structure on the sheep brain numbered 2.
	3	Identify the flap like structure on the sheep brain numbered 3.
	4	Identify the nerve on the sheep brain numbered 4.
	5	Identify the nerve on the sheep brain numbered 5.
	6	Identify the nerve on the sheep brain numbered 6.
	7	Identify the structure on the sheep brain numbered 7.
	8	Identify the structure on the sheep brain numbered 8.
13	1	Identify the structure on the x.s. of the sheep brain numbered 1.
	2	Identify the open structure on the x.s. of the sheep brain numbered 2.
14	1	Identify the flap like structure on the sheep brain numbered 1.
	2	Identify the structure on the sheep brain numbered 2.
	3	Identify the structure on the sheep brain numbered 3.
	4	Identify the nerve on the sheep brain numbered 4.
	5	Identify the structure on the sheep brain numbered 5.
	6	Identify the structure on the sheep brain numbered 6.
	7	Identify the lobe on the sheep brain numbered 7.
15	1	Identify the structure on the sheep brain numbered 1.
	2	Identify the structure on the sheep brain numbered 2.
	3	Identify the structure on the sheep brain numbered 3.
	4	Identify the structure on the sheep brain numbered 4.
	5	Identify the structure on the sheep brain numbered 5.
	6	Identify the structure on the sheep brain numbered 6.
	7	Identify the structure on the sheep brain numbered 7.
16	1	Identify the groove on the sheep brain x.s. numbered 1.
	2	Identify the white structure on the sheep brain x.s. numbered 2.
	3	Identify the space on the sheep brain x.s. numbered 3.
	4	Identify the white structure on the sheep brain numbered 4.

	5	Identify the structure on the sheep brain numbered 5.
	6	Identify the structure on the sheep brain numbered 6.
	7	Identify the structure on the sheep brain numbered 7.
	8	Identify the space on the sheep brain numbered 8.
17	1	Identify the structure on the sheep brain numbered 1.
	2	Identify the structure on the sheep brain numbered 2.
	3	Identify the structure on the sheep brain numbered 3.
	4	Identify the structure on the sheep brain numbered 4.
	5	Identify the ventricle on the sheep brain numbered 5.
	6	Identify the structure on the sheep brain numbered 6.
18	1	Identify the ventricle on the sheep brain numbered 1.
	2	Identify the structure on the sheep brain numbered 2.
	3	Identify the structure on the sheep brain numbered 3.
	4	Identify the structure on the sheep brain numbered 4.
	5	Identify the structure on the sheep brain numbered 5.
	6	Identify the structure on the sheep brain numbered 6.
	7	Identify the structure on the sheep brain numbered 7.
	8	Identify the structure on the sheep brain numbered 8.
	9	Identify the structure on the sheep brain numbered 9.
	10	Identify the structure on the sheep brain numbered 10
19	1	Identify the structure on the sheep brain numbered 1.
	2	Identify the structure on the sheep brain numbered 2.
	3	Identify the structure on the sheep brain numbered 3.
	4	Identify the structure on the sheep brain numbered 4.
	5	Identify the structure on the sheep brain numbered 5.
	6	Identify the structure on the sheep brain numbered 6.
	7	Identify the structure on the sheep brain numbered 7.
	8	Identify the structure on the sheep brain numbered 8.
	9	Identify the structure on the sheep brain numbered 9.
	10	Identify the white structure on the sheep brain numbered 10.
	11	Identify the membrane structure on the sheep brain numbered 11.
	12	Identify the structure on the sheep brain numbered 12.
	13	Identify the structure on the sheep brain numbered 13.
	14	Identify the anatomical part of the sheep brain numbered 14.
	15	Identify the meninx on the sheep brain numbered 15.
20		NO QUESTION

Type **HUMANBRAIN** in white space in tool bar to bring up these images

Picture #	Question #	Questions
01	1	Identify the bump on the human brain model numbered 1.
	2	Identify the depression on the human brain model numbered 2.
	3	Identify the lobe on the human brain model numbered 3.
	4	Identify the lobe on the human brain model numbered 4.
	5	Identify the lobe on the human brain model numbered 5.
	6	Identify the lobe on the human brain model numbered 6.
	7	Identify the structure on the human brain model numbered 7.
02	1	Identify the structure on the human brain model numbered 1.
	2	Identify the nerve on the human brain model numbered 2.
	3	Identify the structure on the human brain model numbered 3.
	4	Identify the nerve on the human brain model numbered 4.
	5	Identify the structure on the human brain model numbered 5.
	6	Identify the nerve on the human brain model numbered 6.
	7	Identify the structure on the human brain model numbered 7.
	8	Identify the nerve on the human brain model numbered 8.
03	1	Identify the sulcus on the human brain model numbered 1.
	2	Identify the sulcus on the human brain model numbered 2.
	3	Identify the lobe on the human brain model numbered 3.
	4	Identify the lobe on the human brain model numbered 4.
	5	Identify the lobe on the human brain model numbered 5.
	6	Identify the lobe on the human brain model numbered 6.
	7	Identify the structure on the human brain model numbered 7.
	8	Identify the indentation on the human brain model numbered 8.
	9	Identify the small bumps on the human brain model numbered 9.
04	1	Identify the specific area and indicate its function that is purple in color and numbered 1.
	2	Identify the specific area and indicate its function that is green in color and numbered 2.
	3	Identify the specific area and indicate its function that is red in color and numbered 3.
05	1	Identify the structure on the human brain model numbered 1.
	2	Identify the structure on the human brain model numbered 2.
	3	Identify the structure on the human brain model numbered 3.
	4	Identify the nerve numbered 4.
06	1	Identify the lobe and functions of the red area lettered A.
	2	Identify the lobe and functions of the red area lettered B.
	3	Identify the lobe and functions of the blue area lettered C.
	4	Identify the lobe and functions of the green area lettered D.
	5	Identify the lobe and functions of the yellow area lettered E.

	6	Identify the structure and its functions of the brown area lettered F.
07	1	Identify the lobe on the human brain model numbered 1.
	2	Identify the structure on the human brain model numbered 2.
	3	Identify the lobe on the human brain model numbered 3.
	4	Identify the lobe on the human brain model numbered 4.
	5	Identify the depression on the human brain model numbered 5.
	6	Identify the structure on the human brain model numbered 6.
	7	Identify the structure on the human brain model numbered 7.
	8	Identify the membrane covering on the human brain model numbered 8.
	9	Identify the structure on the human brain model numbered 9.
	10	Identify the structure on the human brain model numbered 10.
	11	Identify the structure on the human brain model numbered 11.
	12	Identify the structure on the human brain model numbered 12.
	13	Identify the structure on the human brain model numbered 13.
08	1	Identify the structure on the human brain model numbered 1.
	2	Identify the structure on the human brain model numbered 2.
	3	Identify the structure on the human brain model numbered 3.
	4	Identify the structure on the human brain model numbered 4.
	5	Identify the structure on the human brain model numbered 5.
	6	Identify the structure on the human brain model numbered 6.
	7	Identify the structure on the human brain model numbered 7.
	8	Identify the structure on the human brain model numbered 8.
	9	Identify the ventricle on the human brain model numbered 9.
	10	Identify the structure on the human brain model numbered 10.
09	1	Identify the space on the human brain model numbered 1.
	2.	Identify the meninx on the human brain model numbered 2.
	3	Identify the meninx on the human brain model numbered 3.
	4	Identify the space on the human brain model numbered 4.
	5	Identify the meninx on the human brain model numbered 5.
	6	Identify the structure on the human brain model numbered 6.
10	1	Identify the large depression on the human brain model numbered 1.
	2	Identify the structure on the human brain model numbered 2.
	3	Identify the depression on the human brain model numbered 3.
	4	Identify the lobe on the human brain model numbered 4.
	5	Identify the structure on the human brain model numbered 5.

BRAIN STEM MODEL
Type **BRAINSTEM** in white space in tool bar to bring up these images

Picture #	Question #	Questions
01	1	Identify the structure on the brain stem model numbered 1.
	2	Identify the structure on the brain stem model numbered 2.
	3	Identify the structure on the brain stem model numbered 3.
	4	Identify the structure on the brain stem model numbered 4.
	5	Identify the anatomical portion of the brain stem model numbered 5.
	6	Identify the anatomical portion of the brain stem model numbered 6.
02	1	Identify the anatomical portion of the brain stem model numbered 1.
	2	Identify the anatomical portion of the brain stem model numbered 2.
	3	Identify the structure on the brain stem model numbered 3.
	4	Identify the structure on the brain stem model numbered 4.
	5	Identify the blood vessels on the brain stem model numbered 5.
	6	Identify the structure on the brain stem model numbered 6.
03	1	Identify the structure on the brain stem model numbered 1.
	2	Identify the structure on the brain stem model numbered 2.
	3	Identify the structure on the brain stem model numbered 3.
	4	Identify the structure on the brain stem model numbered 4.
	5	Identify the structure on the brain stem model numbered 5.
	6	Identify the structure on the brain stem model numbered 6.
	7	Identify the structure on the brain stem model numbered 7.
	8	Identify the structure on the brain stem model numbered 8.
	9	Identify the structure on the brain stem model numbered 9.
04	1	Identify the nerve on the brain stem model numbered 1.
	2	Identify the structure on the brain stem model numbered 2.
	3	Identify the structure on the brain stem model numbered 3.
	4	Identify the structure on the brain stem model numbered 4.
	5	Identify the nerve on the brain stem model numbered 5.

BRAIN VENTRICLE
MODELS
Type **BRAINVENT** in white space in tool bar to bring up these images

Picture #	Question #	Questions
01	1	Identify the ventricles on the model numbered 1.
	2	Identify the ventricle on the model numbered 2.
	3	Identify the structure on the model numbered 3.
	4	Identify the structure on the model numbered 4.
	5	Identify the ventricle on the model numbered 5.

02	1	Identify the ventricle on the model numbered 1.
	2	Identify the ventricle on the model numbered 2.
	3	Identify the structure on the model numbered 3.
	4	Identify the structure on the model numbered 4.
03	1	Identify the ventricles on the model numbered 1.
	2	Identify the ventricle on the model numbered 2.
	3	Identify the structure on the model numbered 3.
	4	Identify the structure on the model numbered 4.
04	1	Identify the ventricles on the model numbered 1.
	2	Identify the ventricle on the model numbered 2.
	3	Identify the structure on the model numbered 3
	4	Identify the structure on the model numbered 4.

SPINAL CORD MODELS
Type **SPINALCORD** in white space in tool bar to bring up these images

Picture #	Question #	Questions
01	1	Identify the part of the spinal cord numbered 1.
	2	Identify the long slit on the spinal cord numbered 2.
	3	Identify the specific part of the spinal cord numbered 3.
	4	Identify the specific part of the spinal cord numbered 4.
	5	Identify the specific part of the spinal cord numbered 5.
	6	Identify the specific part of the spinal cord numbered 6.
	7	The nerve numbered 7 on the spinal cord is an (sensory or motor) nerve.
	8	Identify the nerve part numbered 8 on the spinal cord model.
	9	Identify the part of the spinal cord numbered 9.
	10	The nerve numbered 10 on the spinal cord is an (sensory or motor) nerve.
	11	Identify the white structure on the spinal cord model numbered 11.
02	1	Identify the specific blue structure on the spinal cord numbered 1.
	2	Identify the specific gray structure on the spinal cord numbered 2.
	3	Identify the specific pink membrane on the spinal cord numbered 3.
	4	Identify the space on the spinal cord model lettered "A".
	5	Identify the space on the spinal cord model lettered "B".
	6	Identify the space on the spinal cord model lettered "C".
03	1	Identify the specific part on the spinal cord model lettered 1.
	2	Identify the specific part on the spinal cord model lettered 2.
	3	Identify the hole on the spinal cord model numbered 3.
	4	What fluid is contained with the part numbered 3 on the spinal cord model?
04	1	Identify the structure on the spinal cord model numbered 1.

	2	Identify the specific part on the spinal cord model numbered 2.
	3	Identify the specific part on the spinal cord model numbered 3.
	4	Identify the specific part on the spinal cord model numbered 4.
	5	Identify the specific part on the spinal cord model numbered 5.
	6	Identify the specific part on the spinal cord model numbered 6.
	7	Identify the specific part on the spinal cord model numbered 7.
	8	Identify the specific part of the spinal cord model numbered 8.
	9	Identify the specific part of the spinal cord model numbered 9.
05	1	Identify the specific part of the spinal cord model numbered 1.
	2	Identify the specific part of the spinal cord model numbered 2.
	3	Identify the specific part of the spinal cord model numbered 3.
	4	Identify the hole on the spinal cord model numbered 4.
	5	Identify the specific part of the spinal cord model numbered 5.
	6	Identify the specific part of the spinal cord model numbered 6.
06	1	Identify the specific part of the spinal cord model numbered 1.
	2	Identify the specific part of the spinal cord model numbered 2.
	3	Identify the specific part of the spinal cord model numbered 3.
	4	Identify the specific part of the spinal cord model numbered 4.
	5	Identify the hole on the spinal cord model numbered 5.
	6	Identify the specific part of the spinal cord model numbered 6.
	7	Identify the neuron on the spinal cord model numbered 7.
	8	Identify the neuron on the spinal cord model numbered 8.
	9	Identify the structure on the spinal cord model numbered 9.
	10	Identify the long slit on the spinal cord model numbered 10.
07		REVIEW AFFERENT AND EFFERENT NEURONS ON THIS MODEL
08	1	Identify the lobe of the brain on the spinal cord model numbered 1.
	2	Identify the lobe of the brain on the spinal cord model numbered 2.
	3	Identify the lobe of the brain on the spinal cord model numbered 3.
	4	Identify the lobe of the brain on the spinal cord model numbered 4.
	5	Identify the structure of the brain on the spinal cord model numbered 5.
	6	Identify the enlargement on the spinal cord model numbered 6.
	7	Identify the enlargement on the spinal cord model numbered 7.
	8	Identify the part of the spinal cord model numbered 8.
	9	Identify the part of the spinal cord model numbered 9.
	10	Identify the part of the spinal cord model numbered 10.
09	1	Identify the nerve plexus on the spinal cord model numbered 1.
	2	Identify the specific nerve on the spinal cord model numbered 2.
	3	Identify the nerve plexus on the spinal cord model numbered 3.

	4	Identify the enlargement on the spinal cord model numbered 4.
	5	Identify the specific groove on the brain numbered 5.
	6	Identify the specific groove on the brain numbered 1.
10	1	Identify the meninx on the spinal cord model numbered 1.
	2	Identify the meninx on the spinal cord model numbered 2.
	3	Identify the meninx on the spinal cord model numbered 3.
	4	Identify the space on the spinal cord model numbered 4.
	5	Identify the space on the spinal cord model numbered 5.
	6	Identify the space on the spinal cord model numbered 6.
11	1	Identify the specific part of the spinal cord model numbered 1.
	2	Identify the nerve plexus on the spinal cord model numbered 2.
	3	Identify the specific group of nerves on the spinal cord model numbered 3.
	4	Identify the nerve plexus on the spinal cord model numbered 4.
	5	Identify the specific structure on the spinal cord model numbered 5.
	6	Identify the specific nerve on the spinal cord model numbered 6.
12	1	Identify the specific nerve plexus on the spinal cord model numbered 1.
	2	Identify the specific nerve plexus on the spinal cord model numbered 2.
	3	Identify the specific nerve plexus on the spinal cord model numbered 3.
	4	Identify the specific nerve plexus on the spinal cord model numbered 4.
	5	Identify the enlargement on the spinal cord model numbered 5.
	6	Identify the enlargement on the spinal cord model numbered 6.
	7	Identify the structure on the spinal cord model numbered 7.
	8	Identify the group of nerves on the spinal cord model numbered 8.
	9	Identify the skeletal structure on the spinal cord model numbered 9.
	10	Identify the non-neural membrane structure on the spinal cord model numbered 10.
	11	Identify the nerve on the spinal cord model numbered 11.
	12	Identify the nerve on the spinal cord model numbered 12.
	13	Identify the nerve on the spinal cord model numbered 13.
	14	Identify the nerve on the spinal cord model numbered 14.
13	1	Identify the enlargement on the spinal cord model numbered 1.
	2	Identify the long grove on the spinal cord model numbered 2.
	3	Identify the pinkish bump on the spinal cord model numbered 3.
	4	Identify the specific nerve plexus on the spinal cord model numbered 4.
	5	Identify the specific nerve on the spinal cord model numbered 5.
	6	Identify the specific nerve plexus on the spinal cord model numbered 6.
	7	Identify the pinkish bump on the spinal cord model numbered 7.
	8	Identify the group of white strings on the spinal cord model numbered 8.
14	1	Identify the white structure on the spinal cord model numbered 1.

	2	Identify the specific area on the spinal cord model numbered 2.
	3	Identify the group of white structures on the spinal cord model numbered 3.
	4	Identify the specific white structure on the spinal cord model numbered 4.
	5	Identify the pinkish structure on the spinal cord model numbered 5.
15	1	Identify the specific area on the spinal cord model numbered 1.
	2	Identify the group of nerves on the spinal cord model numbered 2.
	3	Identify the specific structure on the spinal cord model numbered 3.
	4	Identify the specific nerve plexus on the spinal cord model numbered 4.
	5	Identify the specific nerve plexus on the spinal cord model numbered 5.
	6	Identify the specific nerve on the spinal cord model numbered 6.
	7	Identify the specific nerve on the spinal cord model numbered 7.
	8	Identify the pinkish structure on the spinal cord model numbered 8.

NERVOUS
HISTOLOGY
Type **NERVEHIST** in white space in tool bar to bring up these images

Picture #	Question #	Question
01	1	Identify this tissue.
	2	Identify the structure numbered 2.
	3	Identify the specific cells (dots) numbered 8.
02	1	Identify the hole numbered 1.
	2	Identify the slit numbered 2.
	3	Identify the specific part numbered 3.
	4	Identify the specific part numbered 4.
	5	Identify the specific area on the spinal cord numbered 5.
03	1	Identify this tissue.
	2	Identify the structure (dark lines) with the cell numbered 2.
	3	Identify the structure (dark mass) numbered 3.
04	1	Identify the cell numbered 1.
	2	Identify the part numbered 2.
05	1	Identify the structure numbered 1.
	2	Identify the structure numbered 2.
	3	Identify the structure (black disk) numbered 3.
	4	Identify the structure numbered 4.

EYE
Type **EYE** in white space in tool bar to bring up these images

Picture #	Question #	Questions

01	1	Identify the specific layer of the eye numbered 1.
	2	Identify the structure on the eye model numbered 2.
	3	Identify the structure on the eye model numbered 3.
	4	Identify the specific layer on the eye model numbered 4.
	5	Identify the specific layer on the eye model numbered 5.
	6	Identify the specific layer on the eye model numbered 6.
	7	Identify the hole on the eye model numbered 7.
	8	Identify the specific skeletal muscle on the eye model numbered 8.
02	1	Identify the specific layer on the eye model numbered 1.
	2	Identify the specific layer on the eye model numbered 2.
	3	Identify the specific layer on the eye model numbered 3.
	4	Identify the specific layer on the eye model numbered 4.
	5	Identify structure on the eye model numbered 5.
	6	Identify the specific smooth muscle on the eye model numbered 6.
	7	Identify the string like structures on the eye model numbered 6.
	8	Identify the structure on the eye model numbered 8.
03	1	Identify the structure on the eye model numbered 1.
	2	Identify the yellow structure on the eye model numbered 2.
	3	Identify the green area on the eye model numbered 3.
04	1	Identify the layer on the eye model numbered 1.
	2	Identify the layer on the eye model numbered 2.
	3	Identify the layer on the eye model numbered 3.
	4	Identify the specific area on the eye model numbered 4.
	5	Identify the structure on the eye model numbered 5.
	6	Identify the structure on the eye model numbered 6.
	7	Identify the structure on the eye model numbered 7.
05	1	Identify the structure on the eye model numbered 1.
	2	Identify the hole on the eye model numbered 2.
06	1	Identify the specific chamber on the eye model numbered 1.
	2	Identify the cavity on the eye model numbered 2.
07	1	Identify the structure on the eye model numbered 1.
	2	Identify the structure on the eye model numbered 2.
	3	Identify the structure on the eye model numbered 3.
	4	Identify the opening on the eye model numbered 4.
	5	Identify the specific skeletal eye muscle numbered 5.
	6	Identify the specific skeletal eye muscle numbered 6.
	7	Identify the specific skeletal eye muscle numbered 7.
	8	Identify the specific skeletal eye muscle numbered 8.

08	1	Identify the specific skeletal eye muscle numbered 1.
	2	Identify the specific skeletal eye muscle numbered 2.
	3	Identify the specific skeletal eye muscle numbered 3.
	4	Identify the specific skeletal eye muscle numbered 4.
	5	Identify the specific skeletal eye muscle numbered 5.
09	1	Identify the hole on the eye dissection numbered 1
	2	Identify the specific lens on the eye dissection numbered 2.
	3	Identify the dark structure on the eye dissection numbered 3.
10	1	Identify the specific structure on the eye dissection numbered 1.
	2	Identify the layer on the eye dissection numbered 2.
11	1	Identify the structure as seen through an ophthalmoscope numbered 1.
	2	Identify the structure as seen through an ophthalmoscope numbered 2.
	3	Identify the structure as seen through an ophthalmoscope numbered 3.
12	1	Identify the structure as seen through an ophthalmoscope numbered 1.
	2	Identify the structure as seen through an ophthalmoscope numbered 2.
	3	Identify the structure as seen through an ophthalmoscope numbered 3.
13		REVIEW LATRAL VIEW OF SHEEP EYE DISSECTION

EAR

Type **EAR.** in white space in tool bar to bring up these images

Picture #	Question #	Questions
01	1	Identify the structure on the ear model numbered 1.
	2	Identify the structure on the ear model numbered 2.
	3	Identify the coiled structure on the ear model numbered 3.
	4	Identify the structure on the ear model numbered 4.
	5	Identify the structure on the ear model numbered 5.
02	1	Identify the division of the ear model numbered 1.
	2	Identify the division of the ear model numbered 2.
	3	Identify the division of the ear model numbered 3.
03	1	Identify the structure on the ear model numbered 1.
	2	Identify the structure on the ear model numbered 2.
	3	Identify the membrane structure on the ear model numbered 3.
	4	Identify the bone on the ear model numbered 4.
	5	Identify the structure on the ear model numbered 5.
	6	Identify the structure on the ear model numbered 6.
	7	Identify the structure on the ear model numbered 7.
	8	Identify the structure on the ear model numbered 8.
04	1	Identify the structure numbered 1.
	2	Identify the structure numbered 2.

	3	Identify the structure numbered 3.
	4	Identify the structure numbered 4,
	5	Identify the structure numbered 5.
	6	Identify the structure numbered 6.
	7	Identify the membrane structure numbered 7.
05	1	Identify the structure numbered 1.
	2	Identify the structure numbered 2.
	3	Identify the structure numbered 3.
	4	Identify the structure numbered 4.
	5	Identify the bone numbered 5.
	6	Identify the structure numbered 6.
06	1	Identify the structure numbered 1.
	2	Identify the structure numbered 2.

Blank Page for Notes

ANSWERS
Human Anatomy
& Physiology I

Picture #	Question #	answers
01	1	Left
	2	Right
	3	1. Right forearm – radius should be on the lateral side and the ulna on medial side. 2. Left forearm – ulna should be on the medial side and the radius on the lateral side. 3. Left forearm – The anterior surface of the radius should be facing anterior, not the posterior surface.
02	1	Right
	2	Left
03	1	Anterior
	2	Superior or dorsal
	3	Posterior or caudal
	4.	Inferior or ventral
	5.	Right
04	1	Anterior surface of left leg
	2	Lateral surface of right leg
05	1	Superior
	2.	Lateral
	3.	Medial
	4.	Inferior
	5.	Anterior
	6	Left
06	1	mediastinum
	2.	Mcdial
	3.	Superior
	4	anterior
	5	Right
07	1	Epigastric
	2.	Hypogastric or pubic
	3.	Right hypochondriac
	4.	Left lumbar
	5.	Left iliac or inguinal
	6.	umbilical
08	1	Lateral surface of right leg
	2	Medial surface of left leg
09	A	A
	B	None show in this picture
	C	C
	D	B
10	A	Umbilical
	B	Right iliac (inguinal)
	C	Left lumbar
	D	Hypogastric (pubic)
	E	Epigastric
	F	Right hypochondriac
11.	1	Abdominopelvic cavity
12	1	Right upper quadrant (RUQ)
	2	Left lower quadrant (LLQ)
	3	Left upper quadrant (LUQ)
	4	Right lower quadrant (RLQ)
13	1	Nose (nasal)

	2	Mouth (oral)
	3	Cheek (buccal)
	4	Chin (mental)
	5	Neck (cervical)
	6	Front of elbow (antecubital)
	7	Arm (brachial)
	8	Forearm (antebrachial)
	9	Wrist (carpal)
	10	Chest (thoracic)
	11	Abdominal (abdomen) or Navel (umbilical)
	12	Palm (metacarpal or palmar)
	13	Thumb (pollex0 which is 1st digit or phalangeal
	14	Fingers (phalange)
	15	2nd digit (phalanx)
	16	Thigh (femoral)
	17	Anterior surface of knee (patellar)
	18	Toes (digital or phalanges), specifically 3rd digit (phalanx)
	19	Great toe (hallux) which is 1st digit
	20	Armpit (axillary)
14	1	Left leg (anterior view)
	2	Right arm (anterior view)
	3	Right leg (posterior view)
	4	Left arm (posterior view)
	5	Posterior surface of left leg (posterior view)
	6	Anterior surface of right leg (anterior view)
	7	Posterior surface of left hand (posterior view)
	8	Anterior surface of right palm (anterior view)
	9	Lateral surface of left arm (anterior view)
	10	Medial surface of left arm (anterior view)
	11	Superior surface of right foot (anterior view)
	12	Posterior surface of right foot or calcaneal (heal) on posterior view
	13	The elbow ("A") is proximal to the wrist ("B"). The letter "A" is superior to the letter "B". The letter "B" is inferior to the letter "A"
15	1	Superior surface
	2	Medial surface
	3	Lateral surface
	4	Inferior surface
	5	(b) left lung. Every thing is always in anatomical position (AP).
	6	Mediastinum
16	1	Right upper quadrant (RUQ)
	2	Left lower quadrant (LLQ)
	3	Hypogastric (pubic) region of nine
	4	Epigastric region of nine
	5	Right lumbar region of nine
	6	Umbilical region of nine
	7	Visceral pleura
	8	Visceral peritoneum

EPITHELIAL CELL
MODELS

Picture #	Question #	answers
01	1	Squamous
	2	Nucleus
02	1	Cuboidal
	2	Nucleus
03	1	Columnar
	2	Nucleus
	3	Simple
04	1	Columnar
	2	Cilia
	3	Pseudostratified

EPITHELIAL HISTOLOGY
PICTURES

Picture #	Question #	answers
01	1	Epithelial tissue
	2	Squamous epithelial cells
02	1	Squamous epithelial cells
	2	Nucleus
03	1	Epithelial tissue
	2	Cuboidal epithelial cells
	3	Simple cuboidal epithelium tissue
	4	Nucleus of cuboidal cell
04	1	Columnar epithelial cells
	2	Goblet cell (produces mucus)
05	1	Stratified transitional epithelium
	2	Free surface
06	1	Keratinized stratified squamous epithelium
07	1	Cuboidal epithelial cell
	2	Nucleus
08	1	Simple cuboidal
	2	Simple
	3	Apical (free) surface (facing free surface)
	4	Basal surface (attached to the basement membrane)
09	1	Transitional epithelium
	2	Basement membrane
10	1	Columnar epithelium cell

Picture #	Question #	answers
11	1	Villi of small intestine
12	1	Epithelial tissue
	2	Columnar epithelial cell
	3	Goblet cell (modified columnar epithelial cell that produces mucus)
13	1	Ciliated pseudostratified columnar epithelium
14	1	Ciliated pseudostratified columnar epithelium tissue
	2	Cilia
15	1	Stratified squamous epithelial tissue

CONNECTIVE TISSUE
HISTOLOGY

Picture #	Question #	answers
01	1	Areolar connective tissue
	2	Collagenous (white) fiber
	3	Elastic fiber
02	1	Loose (areolar connective tissue)
	2	Elastic fiber
03	1	Reticular connective tissue
	2	Reticular fiber
04	1	Adipose tissue
05	1	Irregular dense connective tissue
06	1	Collagenous (white) fiber
07	1	Regular dense connective tissue (ligament or tendon)
08	1	Cartilage
	2	Lacunae
	3	Nucleus of chondrocyte
09	1	Hyaline cartilage
	2	Lacuna
	3	Nucleus of chondrocyte
	4	Ground substance of cartilage
10	1	Elastic cartilage
11	1	Hyaline cartilage
12	1	Compact bone
	2	Haversian (Central) canal
	3	Osteocytes
13	1	Haversian (Central) canal
	2	Volkmann's (perforating) canal
14	1	Osteocyte (bone cell) in lacunae
	2	Canaliculi

	3	Haversian (Central) canal
	4	Volkmann's (peforating) canal
15	1	Compact bone
16	1	Osteocyte in lacunae
	2	Canaliculi
	3	Volkmann's (perforating) canal
17	1	Compact bone
	2	Lamella
	3	Osteon of compact bone
18	1	Cartilage
	2	Lacunae
	3	Chondrocyte
19	1	Adipose tissue
	2	Adipose (adipocyte) cell
20	1	Adipose tissue
21	1	Nuclei of fibroblast

INTEGUMENTARY SYSTEM (SKIN)

Picture #	Question #	answers
01	1	Stratum corneum of epidermis
	2	Epidermis
	3	Dermal papillae
	4	Papillary region (layer) of dermis
	5	Reticular region (layer) of dermis
	6	Hair shaft
	7	Sebaceous (oil) gland producing sebum
	8	Arrector pili muscle
	9	Gland portion of Sudoriferous (sweat) gland
	10	Duct portion of sudoriferous (sweat) gland
	11	Adipose tissue
	12	Pacinian corpuscle (respond to heavy pressure)
	13	Meissner's corpuscle (respond to light pressure)
	14	Dermis
	15	Hypodermis (subcutaneous layer or superficial fascia)

SKELETON SYSTEM
BASIC BONE STRUCTURE

Picture #	Question #	answer
01	1	Epiphysis
	2	Metaphysis
	3	Diaphysis (shaft)
02	1	Compact (dense)
	2	Spongy (cancellous)
	2A	Marrow (red or yellow)
	3	Medullary cavity
03	1	Medullary cavity
	2	Compact (dense)

AXIAL SKELETON
SKULL

Picture #	Question #	answers
01	1	coronal
	2	Sagittal
	3	Frontal
	4	Parietal
02	1	Lambdoid
	2	Sagittal
	3	Parietal
	4	Occipital
03	1	Sagittal
	2	Coronal
	3	Lambdoid
	4	Frontal
	5	Parietal
	6	Occipital
04	1	Temporal
	2	Occipital
	3	Parietal
	4	Frontal
	5	Sagittal
	6	Lambdoid
05	1	Frontal
	2	Zygomatic
	3	Maxilla

		4	Nasal
		5	Greater wing of sphenoid
		6	Zygomatic process of frontal bone
		7	Zygomatic process of maxilla
		8	Maxillary process of zygomatic bone
		9	Frontal process of zygomatic bone
		10	Superior orbital fissure
		11	Infraorbital foramen
		12	Intramaxillary suture (synostosis suture)
		13	Inferior nasal concha
06		1	Right nasal bone
		2	Left nasal bone
07		1	Supraorbital foramen (notch)
		2	Inferior orbital fissure of maxillary bone
		3	Superior orbital fissure of sphenoid bone
		4	Infraorbital foramen
		5	Inferior nasal concha
		6	Mental foramen of mandible
		7	Vomer (forms inferior portion of nasal septum)
		8	Perpendicular plate of ethmoid (forms superior portion of nasal septum)
		9	Frontal
		10	Nasal
		11	Maxilla
		12	Mandible
08			Frontal
09		1	Inferior nasal concha
		2	Vomer
		3	Middle nasal concha
		4	Superior nasal fissure
		5	Perpendicular plate of ethmoid
		6	Zygomatic
10		1	Frontal
		2	Parietal
		3	Occipital
		4	Squamous portion of temporal bone
		5	Greater wing of sphenoid
		6	Zygomatic
		7	Maxilla

	8	Lacrimal
	9	Nasal
	10	Styloid process
	11	Pterygoid process of sphenoid
	12	Mastoid process
	13	External auditory meatus
11	1	Zygomatic
	2	Nasal
	3	Maxilla
	4	Lacrimal
	5	Ethmoid
	6	Sphenoid
12	1	Zygomatic process of frontal bone
	2	Supraorbital foramen
	3	Lacrimal
	4	Inferior orbital fissure
	5	Nasal
	6	Vomer
13	1	Frontal
	2	Parietal
	3	Zygomatic process of temporal bone
	4	Mastoid process of temporal bone
	5	Squamous process of temporal bone
	6	Occipital
	7	Greater wing of sphenoid
14	1	Ramus of mandible
	2	Mandibular condyle (articulates to mandibular fossa of temporal bone forming temporomandibular joint "TMJ")
	3	Coronoid process
	4	Angle of mandible
	5	Crown of molar
	6	Root of molar within alveoli (tooth socket)
	7	Mental foramen
15	1	Mastoid process of temporal bone
	2	Styloid process temporal bone
	3	External auditory meatus of temporal bone

	4	Zygomatic process of temporal bone
	5	Wormian (Sutural) bones (named after the a Dutch anatomist, O. Wormian. These bones are small bones located within the joints (sutures) of certain cranial bones. Their number varies greatly from person to person.

16	1	Parietal
	2	Occipital
17	1	Mandibular notch of temporal bone
	2	Mastoid process of temporal bone
	3	Mandibular condyle
	4	Coronoid process
	5	Ramus of mandible
	6	Mental foramen
18	1	Mastoid process
	2	External auditory meatus
	3	Alveoli in maxilla
	4	Zygomatic
	5	Zygomatic process of temporal bone
19	1	External auditory meatus
	2	Styloid process of temporal bone
	3	Mastoid process of temporal bone
	4	Zygomatic process of temporal bone
	5	Greater wing of sphenoid bone
	6	Zygomatic process of frontal bone
	7	Squamous process of temporal bone
	8	Zygomatic
20	1	Foramen magnum
	2	Occipital condyle
	3	Mandibular fossa of temporal bone
	4	Foramen ovale
	5	Jugular foramen
	6	Carotid foramen
	7	Foramen lacerum
	8	Palatine process of maxilla
	9	horizontal process of palatine bone
	10	Occipital
	11	Greater wing sphenoid bone
	12	Petrous portion of temporal bone
21	1	Alveoli of maxilla
	2	Incisive fossa (foramen)
	3	Petrous portion
	4	Carotid canal (foramen)
	5	Foramen ovale

	6	Foramen lacerum
	7	Palatine process of maxilla
	8	Horizontal process of palatine bone
	9	Mandibular fossa
	10	Zygomatic process of temporal bone
	11	Foramen magnum
	12	Occipital
	13	Occipital condyle
	14	Vomer
	15	Pterygoid process of sphenoid bone
22	1	Jugular foramen
	2	Foramen lacerum
	3	Carotid foramen (canal)
	4	Foramen ovale
	5	Mandibular fossa
	6	Occipital condyle
	7	Occipital
23	1	Foramen magnum
	2	Occipital condyle
	3	Mastoid process of temporal bone
	4	Jugular foramen
	5	Carotid foramen (canal)
	6	Foramen lacerum
	7	Jugular foramen
	8	Mandibular fossa
	9	Vomer
	10	Occipital
	11	Carotid foramen (canal)
24	1	Alveoli in maxilla
	2	Incisive foramen
	3	Foramen lacerum
	4	Carotid foramen (canal)
	5	Palatine process of maxilla
	6	Horizontal plate of palatine bone
	7	Pterygoid process
25	1	Mandible
	2	Mandibular condyle
	3	Coronoid process
26	1	Coronoid process

	2	Mandibular condyle
	3	Ramus of mandible
	4	Mental foramen
	5	Body
	6	Angle
	7	Alveolar margin
27	1	Angle
	2	Ramus of mandible
	3	Mental foramen
	4	Alveolar margin containing alveoli (tooth socket)
	5	Body of mandible
28	1	Body of mandible
	2	Mental foramen
	3	Alveolar
	4	Mandibular condyle
29	1	Pterygoid process of sphenoid bone
	2	Vomer
	3	Alveolar
	4	Incisive fossa (foramen)
	5	Maxilla
	6	Palatine
30	1	Frontal
	2	Crista galli of ethmoid bone
	3	Lesser wing of sphenoid
	4	Optic foramen (canal)
	5	Squamous portion of temporal bone
	6	Sella turcica or (hypophyseal fossa) of sphenoid bone
	7	Foramen ovale
	8	Petrous portion of temporal bone
	9	Jugular foramen
	10	Occipital
	11	Foramen magnum
31	1	Crista galli of ethmoid bone
	2	Frontal
	3	Foramen ovale
	4	Optic foramen (canal)
	5	Sella turcica or (hypophyseal fossa) of sphenoid bone
	6	Foramen lacerum
	7	Hypoglossal canal

	8	Jugular foramen
	9	Lesser wing of sphenoid
32	1	Crista galli
	2	Foramen ovale
	3	Foramen lacerum
	4	Jugular foramen
	5	Internal acoustic meatus
	6	Sella turcica or (hypophyseal fossa) of sphenoid bone
	7	Lesser wing of sphenoid
	8	Optic foramen (canal)
	9	Hypoglossal canal
33	1	Zygomatic process of temporal bone
	2	Squamous portion of temporal
	3	Mastoid process of temporal
	4	External auditory meatus
	5	Mandibular fossa
34	1	Squamous portion of temporal
	2	Petrous portion of temporal
	3	Internal acoustic meatus
35	1	Crista galli
	2	Orbital plate (lateral mass)
	3	Middle nasal concha
	4	Ethmoid sinuses
36		Petrous portion of temporal bone
37	1	Lesser wing of sphenoid
	2	Greater wing of sphenoid
	3	Sphenoid sinuses
	4	Pterygoid process
38	1	Optic canal (foramen)
	2	Foramen spinosum
	3	Body
	4	Foramen ovale
	5	Greater wing
	6	Sella turcica or (hypophyseal fossa) of sphenoid bone
	7	Lesser wing
39	1	Frontal sinuses
	2	Perpendicular plate of ethmoid
	3	Vomer

	4	Sphenoid sinuses
40	1	Styloid process
	2	Crista galli
	3	Perpendicular plate
	4	Vomer
	5	Frontal
41	1	Perpendicular plate of ethmoid
	2	Middle nasal concha
	3	Orbital plate
	4	Crista galli
	5	Cribriform plate (part of horizontal plate)
42	1	Occipital condyle
	2	Hypoglossal canal (foramen)
	3	Foramen magnum
43	1	Frontal (anterior) fontanel
	2	Coronal suture
	3	Sagittal suture
44	1	Mastoid (posterior lateral) fontanel
	2	Sphenoidal (anterior lateral) fontanel
45	1	Occipital (posterior)
	2	Sagittal
46	1	Anterior
	2	Frontal
	3	Coronal
	4	Sagittal
47	1	Hyoid
48	1	Hyoid
	2	2nd cervical (C2) axis
49	1	Inferior nasal conchae
	2	Palatine process of maxilla

VERTEBRAL COLUMN

Picture #	Question #	answers
01	1	Body
	2	Transverse process
	3	Intervertebral disc
	4	sacrum
02	1	Body

	2	Intervertebral disc
	3	Transverse process
03	1	Costal demifacet (facet) for head of rib on thoracic vertebra
	2	Facet for tubercle of rib on thoracic vertebra
	3	Superior articular process
	4	Intervertebral foramen
	5	Body
04	1	Body
	2	Facet for tubercle of rib
	3	Spinous process
	4	Spinal nerve exiting from intervertebral foramen
05	1	Intervertebral foramen
	2	Spinous process
	3	Body of vertebra
	4	Intervertebral disc
	5	Facet for tubercle of rib
	6	Demifacet or costal demifacet for head of rib
06	1	Sacrum
	2	Lumbar (5)
	3	Thoracic (12)
	4	Cervical (7)
	5	Transverse process
	6	Spinous process
07		Lumbar
08		
09		
10	1	Spinous process
	2	Transverse process
	3	Lamina of posterior arch

CERVICAL VERTEBRA

Picture #	Question #	answers
01	1	Transverse process
	2	Superior articular facet (process)
	3	Transverse foramen
	4	Lamina of posterior arch
	5	Dens (odontoid process) of C2
	6	Atlas (C1) anterior view

02	1	Spinous process
	2	Lamina
	3	Inferior articular process
	4	Transverse foramen
	5	Body
	6	Vertebral foramen
	7	C7 (vertebra prominens)
	8	Pedicle
03	1	Spinous process
	2	Body
	3	Lamina
	4	Superior articular process (facet)
	5	Vertebral foramen
	6	Transverse foramen
	7	Pedicle
	8	Transverse process
	9	Transverse foramen
04	1	Dens
	2	Transverse foramen
	3	Superior arch
	4	Transverse process
	5	Superior articular facet (process)
	6	Transverse foramen
	7	Body
	8	Inferior articular facet (process)
	9	Dens (odontoid process)
	10	Spinous process
	11	Dens (odontoid process)
	12	The atlas does not have a body, it becomes the dens of the axis
05	1	Spinous process
	2	Transverse foramen
	3	Transverse process
	4	Lamina
	5	Body
	6	Dens (odontoid process)
	7	Transverse foramen
	8	Transverse process
	9	Superior articular process

	10	Vertebral foramen
06	1	Bifid (split) spinous process
	2	Lamina
	3	Superior articular process
	4	Pedicle
	5	Transverse foramen
	6	Body
	7	Intervertebral disc
	8	Transverse process
07	1	Body
	2	Inferior articular process
	3	Dens (odontoid process)
08	1	Dens (odontoid process)
	2	Superior articular process
	3	Transverse foramen
	4	Facet for dens of axis
09		
10		
11	1	Superior articular process
	2	Dens (odontoid process)
	3	Spinous process
	4	C2 (axis)

THORACIC VERTEBRA

Picture #	Question #	answers
01	1	Spinous process
	2	Lamina
	3	Transverse process
	4	Inferior articular process of thoracic vertebra above this one.
	5	Body
	6	Spinal cord
	7	Tubercle of rib
	8	Head of rib
	9	Pedicle
02	1	Spinous process
	2	Lamina
	3	Transverse process
	4	Superior articular process
	5	Pedicle

	6	Body
	7	Vertebral foramen
03	1	Spinous process
	2	Inferior articular process
	3	Transverse process
	4	Pedicle
	5	Body
	6	Lamina portion of inferior arch
04	1	Facet for tubercle of rib
	2	Spinous process
	3	Inferior articular process
	4	Body
	5	pedicle
	6	Superior articular process

LUMBAR VERTEBRA

Picture #	Question #	answers
01	1	Spinous process
	2	Lamina
	3	Superior articular process
	4	Transverse process
	5	Body
	6	Pedicle
	7	Vertebral foramen

SACRUM and COCCYX

Picture #	Question #	answers
01	1	Superior articular process
	2	Median sacral crest
	3	Dorsal (posterior) sacral foramina
	4	Sacral hiatus
	5	Coccyx
	6	Auricular surface for articulating with the ilium of each hipbone
02	1	Auricular surface
	2	Ventral (anterior) sacral foramina
	3	Coccyx
	4	Body of second sacral vertebra
03	1	auricular surface
	2	Superior articular process
	3	Coccyx

	4	Median sacral crest
	5	Ilium of pelvic bone
04	1	Body of the first sacral vertebra
	2	Sacral canal
	3	Superior articular process

INDIVIDUAL VERTEBRA

Picture #	Question #	answers
01	1	C1(atlas)
02	1	Sacrum
	2	Coccyx
03	1	Lumbar vertebra
04	1	C2 (axis)
05	1	Thoracic vertebra
O6	1	Typical cervical vertebra
07	1	C2 (axis) superior view

STERNUM

Picture #	Question #	answers
01	1	Manubrium
	2	Body (gladiolus)
	3	Suprasternal (jugular) notch
	4	Clavicular notch
	5	Costal cartilage of first rib
	6	Costal cartilage of fourth rib
02	1	Jugular (suprasternal) notch
	2	Clavicular notch
	3	Costal cartilage of first rib
	4	Body (gladiolus)
03	1	Body (gladiolus)
	2	Costal notches
04	1	Manubrium
	2	Jugular (suprasternal) notch
	3	Clavicular notch
	4	Costal cartilage of first rib
05	1	Suprasternal (jugular) notch
	2	Clavicular notch
	3	Costal cartilage of first rib
06	1	Body
	2	Sternal angle (the junction of the manubrium and body)

	3	Costal notch
	4	Xiphoid process
07	1	Clavicle
	2	manubrium
	3	Body
	4	Xiphoid process
08	1	Body
	2	manubrium
	3	Xiphoid process
	4	Right clavicle
	5	2nd rib
	6	Costal cartilage of 3rd rib
	7	5th rib
	8	9th rib
	9	False (vertebrochondral) rib
09	1	Manubrium
	2	Body
	3	Xiphoid process
	4	Costal cartilage of rib number 2
	5	Costal cartilage
	6	Clavicle
	7	3rd right rib

RIBS

Picture #	Question #	answers
01	1	Head
	2	Neck
	3	Tubercle
	4	Costal groove
	5	Body
	6	Angle (costal angle)
02	1	Manubrium
	2	Body
	3	Xiphoid process
	4	True (vertebrosternal) ribs (ribs 1-7)
	5	False (vertebrochondral) ribs (ribs 8-10)
03	1	Superior demifacet (costal demifacet or facet)
	2	Facet for articular part of tubercle of rib
04	1	1st rib

Picture #	Question #	answers
	2	Tubercle
	3	Head
05	1	1, 2, 3, 4, 5, 6, and 7
	2	8, 9, 10
	3	11 and 12 (rib 12 not visible on this picture)
06	1	Tubercle
	2	Head
	3	neck

APPENDICULAR SKELETON
CLAVICLE

Picture #	Question #	answers
01	1	Clavicle
	2	Sternal end (extremity)
	3	Acromial end (extremity)
02	1	Clavicle
	2	Sternal end (extremity)
	3	Acromial end (extremity)
03	1	Manubrium
	2	Sternal end of clavicle
	3	Acromial end of clavicle
	4	Acromion end of scapula
	5	Sternal notch
	6	Jugular (suprasternal) notch
04	1	Sternal end
	2	Acromion end

SCAPULA

Picture #	Question #	answers
01	1	Acromion
	2	Spine
	3	Supraspinous fossa
	4	Infraspinous fossa
	5	Superior angle
	6	Medial (vertebral) border
	7	Inferior angle
	8	Lateral (axillary) border
	9	Glenoid cavity (fossa)
02	1	Glenoid cavity (fossa)
	2	Coracoid process
	3	Acromion

	4	Supraspinous fossa
	5	Body
03	1	Glenoid cavity (fossa)
	2	Acromion
	3	Coracoid process
	4	Subscapular fossa
	5	Scapular notch
04	1	Coracoid process
	2	Acromion
	3	Subscapular fossa
	4	Superior angle
	5	Inferior angle
	6	Glenoid cavity (fossa)
	7	Medial (vertebral) border
	8	Lateral (axillary) border
05	1	Scapula
	2	right

HUMERUS

Picture #	Question #	answers
01	1	Greater tubercle
	2	Lesser tubercle
	3	Surgical neck
	4	Capitulum
	5	Trochlea
	6	Medial epicondyle
	7	Intertubercular sulcus (groove)
	8	Head
	9	Coronoid fossa
	10	Lateral epicondyle
	11	Radial fossa
	12	Deltoid tuberosity
02	1	Lesser tubercle
	2	Greater tubercle
	3	Surgical neck
	4	Intertubercular groove (sulcus)
	5	head
03	1	Capitulum
	2	Trochlea

	3	Medial epicondyle	
	4	Lateral epicondyle	
	5	Radial fossa	
	6	Coronoid process	
	7	Shaft (diaphysis)	
	8	Distal metaphysis	
04	1	Head	
	2	Lesser tubercle	
	3	Greater tubercle	
	4	Intertubercular sulcus (groove)	
	5	Metaphysis portion of bone or (surgical neck area of proximal metaphysis)	
	6	Nutrient foramen	
	7	Anatomical neck	
05	1	Head	
	2	greater tubercle	
	3	Lesser tubercle	
	4	Intertubercular groove	
	5	Surgical neck	
	6	Anatomical neck	
06	1	Medial epicondyle	
	2	Trochlea	
	3	Capitulum	
	4	Lateral epicondyle	
	5	Distal metaphysis	
	6	Coronoid fossa	
	7	Radial fossa	
07	1	Head	
	2	Anatomical neck	
	3	Greater tubercle	
	4	Deltoid tuberosity	
	5	Surgical neck	
08	1	Head	
	2	Greater tubercle	
	3	Anatomical neck	
	4	Surgical neck	
	5	Deltoid tuberosity	
	6	Medial epicondyle	
	7	Trochlea	

	8	Lateral epicondyle
	9	Olecranon fossa
09	1	Medial epicondyle
	2	Trochlea
	3	Lateral epicondyle
	4	Olecranon fossa
10	1	B
11	1	B
12	1	Humerus
	2	left

ULNA

Picture #	Question #	answers
01	1	Styloid process
	2	Head
	3	Radial notch
	4	Olecranon
	5	Coronoid process
	6	Trochlear (semilunar) notch
02	1	Olecranon
	2	Trochlear (semilunar) notch
	3	Coronoid process
	4	Head
	5	Styloid process of ulna
	6	Radial notch (located on lateral surface)
03	1	Olecranon
	2	Coronoid process
	3	Trochlear (semilunar) notch
	4	Radial notch (located on lateral surface)
04	1	Olecranon
	2	Radial notch
	3	Coronoid process
	4	Trochlear (semilunar) notch
05	1	Olecranon
	2	Coronoid process
	3	Radial notch
	4	Trochlear (semilunar) notch
06	1	Ulna
	2	left

Picture #	Question #	answers
01	1	head
	2	Neck of radius
	3	Radial tuberosity (located on medial side)
	4	Styloid process (located on lateral side)
	5	Ulnar notch (located on medial side)
02	1	Head
	2	Neck
	3	Radial tuberosity
	4	Styloid process
	5	Carpals (wrist bones)
03	1	Head
	2	Neck
	3	Radial tuberosity
	4	Styloid process
04	1	Head
	2	Neck
	3	Radial tuberosity
	4	Ulnar notch
	5	Styloid process
05	1	Head
	2	Radial tuberosity
06	1	Styloid process
	2	Concave shape of distal area of shaft colored light pink
07	1	Radius
	2	right

RADIUS and ULNA

Picture #	Question #	answers
01	1	Olecranon of ulna
	2	Coronoid process of ulna
	3	Head of ulna
	4	Radial tuberosity of radius
	5	Trochlear (semilunar) notch of ulna
	6	Styloid process of radius
	7	Head of radius
02	1	Head of radius
	2	Olecranon of ulna
	3	Coronoid process of ulna
	4	Trochlear (semilunar) notch of ulna
	5	Radial tuberosity
03	1	Head of radius
	2	Radial tuberosity of radius
	3	olecranon process of ulna
	4	Trochlear (semilunar) notch of ulna
	5	coronoid process of ulna

HAND

Picture #	Question #	answers
01	1	Base of 3rd metacarpal
	2	Shaft of 3rd metacarpal
	3	Head of 3rd metacarpal. Head forms "kuckles"
	4	Base of 4th proximal phalanx
	5	Shaft of 4th proximal phalanx
	6	Head of 4th proximal phalanx
	7	Base of 3rd middle phalanx
	8	Shaft of 3rd middle phalanx
	9	Head of 3rd middle phalanx
	10	5th distal phalanx
	11	1 (one)
02	1	1st Metacarpal
	2	2nd Metacarpal
	3	3rd Metacarpal
	4	4th metacarpal
	5	5th metacarpal

	6	1st proximal phalanx
	7	2nd proximal phalanx
	8	3rd proximal phalanx
	9	4th proximal phalanx
	10	5th proximal phalanx
	11	2nd middle phalanx
	12	3rd middle phalanx
	13	4th middle phalanx
	14	5th middle phalanx
	15	1st distal phalanx
	16	2nd distal phalanx
	17	3rd distal phalanx
	18	4th distal phalanx
	19	5th distal phalanx
	20	8 carpal (wrist) bones
03	1	1st metacarpal
	2	5th metacarpal
	3	3rd proximal phalanx
	4	4th middle phalanx
	5	2nd distal phalanx
	6	8 carpal (wrist) bones

ULNA, RADIUS and HAND

Picture #	Question #	answers
01	1	Radius (located on lateral side of forearm)
	2	Ulna (located on medial side of forearm)
02	1	Distal portion of radius shaft
	2	Distal portion of ulna shaft
	3	Styloid process of radius
	4	Head of ulna

PELVIC (HIP) BONE

Picture #	Question #	answers
01	1	Iliac crest
	2	Posterior superior iliac spine
	3	Posterior inferior iliac spine
	4	Ischial spine
	5	Anterior superior iliac spine
	6	Anterior inferior iliac spine
	7	Acetabulum

		8	Ischial tuberosity
		9	Pubis
		10	Ilium
		11	Obturator foramen
		12	Lesser sciatic notch
		13	Greater sciatic notch
	02	1	Posterior inferior iliac spine
		2	Posterior superior iliac spine
		3	Anterior superior iliac spine
		4	Anterior inferior iliac spine
		5	Ischial spine
		6	Ilium
		7	Ischium
		8	Pubis
		9	Acetabulum
		10	Iliac crest
		11	Obturator foramen
		12	Greater sciatic notch
		13	Lesser sciatic notch
		14	Ischial tuberosity
	03	1	Pubis
		2	Ischium
		3	Ilium
	04	1	Iliac crest
		2	Ilium
		3	Posterior superior iliac spine
		4	Posterior inferior iliac spine
		5	Ischial spine
		6	Anterior superior iliac spine
		7	Anterior inferior iliac spine
		8	Pubic symphysis
		9	Ramus of pubis
		10	Ischium
		11	Obturator foramen
		12	Auricular surface (articular site for auricular surface on sacrum)
		13	Greater sciatic notch
		14	Lesser sciatic notch
	05	1	Pelvic
		2	right

Picture #	Question #	answers
01	1	Iliac crest
	2	Iliac fossa
	3	Anterior superior iliac spine
	4	Auricular surface
	5	Anterior inferior iliac spine
	6	Pubic symphysis
	7	Ischial spine
	8	Acetabulum
	9	Obturator foramen
	10	Sacrum
	11	Coccyx
02	1	Greater (false) pelvis
	2	Lesser (true) pelvis
03	1	Iliac crest
	2	Posterior superior iliac spine
	3	Posterior inferior iliac spine
	4	Sacrum
	5	Coccyx
	6	Ischial tuberosity
	7	Obturator foramen
	8	Inferior ramus of pubis
	9	Greater sciatic notch
	10	Ischial spine
04	1	Iliac crest
	2	Anterior superior iliac spine
	3	Anterior inferior iliac spine
	4	Acetabulum
	5	Ischial spine
	6	Pubis
	7	Ischial tuberosity
	8	Sacrum
	9	Ilium
	10	Greater sciatic notch
	11	Obturator foramen

FEMUR

Picture #	Question #	answers
01	1	Head
	2	Greater trochanter
	3	Neck
	4	Lesser trochanter
	5	Medial epicondyle
	6	Lateral epicondyle
	7	Patella
02	1	Head
	2	Neck
	3	Greater trochanter
	4	Lesser trochanter
	5	Linea aspera
	6	Lateral condyle
	7	Medial condyle
	8	Intercondylar fossa
03	1	head
	2	Greater trochanter
	3	Lesser trochanter
	4	Medial epicondyle
	5	Neck
04	1	Head
	2	Neck
	3	Greater trochanter
	4	Lesser trochanter
	5	Linea aspera
	6	Medial condyle
	7	Lateral condyle
	8	Intercondylar fossa
	9	Lateral epicondyle
05	1	Head
	2	Neck
	3	Greater trochanter
	4	Lesser trochanter
	5	Nutrient foramina
06	1	Head
	2	Neck
	3	Greater trochanter

	4	Lesser trochanter
07	1	Nutrient foramina
	2	Lateral epicondyle
	3	Medial epicondyle
	4	Patella surface
	5	Lateral condyle
	6	Medial condyle
08	1	Medial epicondyle
	2	Patella surface
	3	Medial condyle
09	1	Lateral condyle
	2	Medial condyle
	3	Intercondylar fossa
	4	Medial epicondyle
	5	Lateral epicondyle
10	1	Epicondyle
	2	Condyle
11	1	Right femur anterior view

PATELLA

Picture #	Question #	answers
01	1	Base of patella
	2	Apex of patella
02	1	Facet of lateral condyle of femur
	2	Facet of medial condyle of femur
	3	Apex of patella
	4	Base of patella
03	1	Base
	2	Apex
04	1	Apex
	2	Facet for lateral condyle
	3	Facet for medial condyle
	4	Base
05	1	Left patella

TIBIA

Picture #	Question #	answers
01	1	Tibial tuberosity
	2	Medial condyle
	3	Medial malleolus

02	1	Medial condyle
	2	Lateral condyle
	3	Intercondylar eminence
	4	Medial malleolus
	5	Fibular notch
03	1	Tibial tuberosity
	2	Medial malleolus
	3	Talus (angle bone) of foot
04	1	Medial condyle
	2	Lateral condyle
	3	Intercondylar eminence or lateral malleolus
	4	Head of fibula
	5	Fibular notch
	6	Talus (angle bone) of foot
	7	Medial malleolus
05	1	Lateral condyle
	2	Medial condyle
	3	Tibial tuberosity
06	1	Medial condyle
	2	Lateral condyle
	3	Intercondylar eminence
	4	Head of fibula
07	1	Medial malleolus
	2	Fibular notch
	3	Talus of foot
08	1	Medial and lateral condyls of tibia or articulation of medial and lateral condylcs of femur
	2	Intercondylar eminence
	3	Condyle of tibia
09	1	Tibia
	2	right

FIBULA

Picture #	Question #	answers
01	1	Head
	2	Mcdial surface of lateral malleolus
02	1	Head
	2	Lateral malleolus
03	1	Head of fibular
	2	Posterior lateral surface of lateral condyle of tibia

04	1	Fibular notch on tibia
05	1	fibula

FOOT

Picture #	Question #	answers
01	1	Talus (angle bone)
	2	Calcaneus (heal bone)
	3	Cuboid
	4	Navicular
	5	Cuneiform (third or lateral)
	6	Metatarsals
	7	Proximal phalanges
	8	Middle phalanx
02	1	Calcaneus
	2	Talus
	3	Navicular
	4	Cuboid
	5	Cuneiforms
	6	5th metatarsal
	7	Base of 2nd metatarsal
	8	Shaft of 2nd metatarsal
	9	Head of 2nd metatarsal
	10	4th proximal phalanx
	11	5th middle phalanx
	12	4th distal phalanx
	13	Base of 1st proximal phalanx (hallux)
	14	Shaft of 1st proximal phalanx (hallux)
	15	Head of 1st proximal phalanx (hallux)
03	1	Tibia
	2	Fibula
	3	Medial malleolus of tibia
	4	Lateral malleolus of fibula
	5	Talus (ankle bone)
04	1	Lateral malleolus of fibula
	2	Calcaneus
	3	Cuboid
	4	5rh metatarsal
	5	Hallux (1st phalanx) "the great or big toe"
05	1	Tibia

	2	Fibula
	3	Lateral malleolus of fibula
	4	Medial malleolus of fibula
	5	Calcaneus
	6	Talus

BONE HISTOLOGY

Picture #	Question #	answers
01	1	Bone
	2	Haversian (central) canal
	3	Osteon
02	1	Lamella
	2	Osteocyte
	3	Canaliculi
03	1	Volkmann's (perforating) canal

JOINTS (ARTICULATION)

Picture #	Question #	answers
01	1	Fibrous joint (subtype gomphosis (periodontal ligament) immobile
0 2	1	Sacroiliac joint (synovial or diarthrotic) subtype plane
03	1	Fibrous joint subtype suture immobile (synarthrosis)
	2	Fibrous joint subtype suture immobile (synarthrosis)
04	1	Acetabulum of hipbone
	2	Head of femur
	3	Greater trochanter
	4	Superior anterior iliac spine
	5	Pubis
	6	Pubic symphysis
05	1	Synarthrotic subtype syndesmosis of distal tibia and fibula
06	1	Patella
	2	Lateral epicondyle
	3	Fibula
	4	Tibia
	5	Head of fibula
	6	Lateral condyle
07	1	Synovial (diarthrotic) subtype pivot of proximal and distal radius and ulnar
08	1	Patella surface on femur
	2	Lateral meniscus (fibrocartilage) covering articular cartilage (hyaline)
	3	Head of fibula
09	1	Synovial (diarthrotic) subtype gliding for scapula and clavicle

	2	Synovial (diarthrotic) subtype plane for scapula gliding over ribs
10	1	Temporomandibular (TMJ) of skull. Synovial (diarthrotic) subtype modified hinge.
11	1	Intercarpal (adjacent carpals) synovial (diarthrotic) subtype plane
12	1	Fingers (interphalangeal) synovial (diarthrotic) subtype hinge
13	1	Knuckles (metacarpophpalangeal) synovial (diarthrotic) subtype condyloid
14	1	Atlas (C1) and axis (C2) synovial (diarthrotic) subtype pivot
15	1	Intervertebral disc located between adjacent vertebral bodies. Cartilaginous (amphiarthrotic) subtype symphysis
16	1	Humerus
	2	Clavicle
	3	Supraspinous fossa
	4	Infraspinous fossa
	5	Acromion
	6	Spine of scapula
	7	Synovial (diarthrotic) subtype ball and socket for shoulder joint
17	1	Elbow (ulna, radius with humerus) synovial (diarthrotic) subtype hinge
18	1	Hip (coxal and femur) synovial (diarthrotic) subtype ball and socket
19	1	Scapula and clavicle. Synovial (diarthrotic) subtype plane
	2	Clavicle and sternum. Synovial (diarthrotic) subtype plane
20	1	Hip (coxal and femur). Synovial (diarthrotic) subtype ball and socket.
21	1	Superior articular process
	2	Dens (odontoid process)
	3	Transverse foramen
	4	C1 and C2 form synovial (diarthrotic) subtype pivot allowing rotation.
22	1	Tibia and fibula (distally). Fibrous (syndesmosis).
23	1	Head of radius
	2	Capitulum of humerus
	3	Coronoid process of ulna
	4	Trochlea of humerus
	5	Radial fossa of humerus
	6	Medial epicondyle
	7	Radial notch on ulna forming proximal radioulnar joint
24	1	Shoulder joint: Synovial (diarthrotic) subtype ball and socket
25	1	Capitulum of humerus
	2	Trochlea of humerus
	3	Medial epicondyle of humerus
	4	Coronoid fossa
	5	Radial fossa
	6	Head of radius

	7	Proximal radioulnar joint. Diarthroses (synovial). Subtype pivot
26	1	Proximal fibula and tibia. Synovial (diarthrotic) subtype plane.
27	1	Olecranon process of ulna
	2	Olecranon fossa of humerus
	3	Trochlea of humerus
	4	Medial epicondyle of humerus
	5	Ulna
	6	Humerus
28	1	Knee (femur and tibia) synovial (diarthrotic) subtype ball and socket.
	2	Femur and patella. Synovial (diarthrotic) subtype plane.
29	1	Radius
	2	Head of radius
	3	Olecranon process of ulna
	4	Trochlear (semilunar) notch of ulna
30	1	Rib to transverse process of vertebra. Synovial (diarthrotic) subtype plane.
31	1	Posterior superior iliac spine of pelvic bone
	2	Posterior inferior iliac spine of pelvic bone
	3	Anterior superior iliac spine of pelvic bone
	4	Anterior inferior iliac spine of pelvic bone
	5	Greater sciatic notch
	6	Head of femur
	7	Acetabulum of pelvic bone
	8	Greater trochanter of femur
32	1	Femur and tibia knee joint. Synovial (diarthrotic) subtype hinge.
	2	Tibia and fibular (proximally) fibrous (syndesmosis) joint

HUMAN SKELETAL MUSCLES

Picture #	Question #	answers
01	1	Digastric
	2	Mylohyoid
	3	Sternocleidomastoid
02	1	Buccinator
03	1	Platysma
04	1	Tensor fasciae latae
	2	Deltoid
	3	Biceps brachii
	4	Triceps brachii (long head)
	5	Sternocleidomastoid
05	1	Diaphragm

	2	Pectoral major
	3	Serratus anterior
	4	Biceps brachii
	5	Pectoralis minor
06	1	Sartorius
	2	Biceps brachii
	3	Triceps brachii
	4	Sternocleidomastoid
	5	Vastus medialis
07	1	Sartorius
	2	Vastus medialis
	3	Rectus femoris
	4	Diaphragm
	5	Serratus anterior
	6	Pectoralis major
	7	Biceps brachii
	8	Triceps brachii
	9	Gracilis
08	1	Vastus medialis
	2	Gastrocnemius
	3	Vastus lateralis
	4	Rectus femoris
	5	Rectus abdominis
	6	Triceps brachii
	7	Biceps brachii
	8	External oblique
09	1	Serratus anterior
	2	Sartorius
	3	Latissimus dorsi
	4	External abdominal oblique
	5	Vastus lateralis
	6	Rectus abdominis
10	1	Sternocleidomastoid
	2	Vastus lateralis
	3	Vastus medialis
	4	Tibialis anterior
	5	Rectus femoris
	6	Pectoralis major

	7	Biceps brachii
	8	Triceps brachii
	9	Deltoid
11	1	Vastus lateralis
	2	Vastus medialis
	3	Rectus femoris
	4	Gracilis
	5	Sartorius
	6	Adductor longus
12	1	Sternocleidomastoid
	2	Sternohyoid
	3	Trapezius
13	1	Pectoralis
	2	Rectus abdominis
	3	External abdominal oblique
	4	Latissimus dorsi
14	1	Trapezius
	2	Teres major
	3	Infraspinatus
	4	Latissimus dorsi
	5	Deltoid
	6	Masseter
15	1	Vastus lateralis
	2	Gluteus maximus
	3	Tensor fasciae latae
	4	Gastrocnemius
	5	Deltoid
	6	Triceps brachii (lateral head)
	7	Soleus
	8	Brachioradialis
	9	Biceps femoris
16	1	Erector spinae group (consists of three groups of muscles – iliocostalis, longissimus, and spinalis).
	2	Supraspinatus
	3	Rhomboideus
17	1	Vastus lateralis
	2	Biceps femoris
	3	Semitendinosus
	4	Semimembranosus

	5	Gracilis
	6	Gastrocnemius
18	1	Gastrocnemius
	2	Soleus
19	1	Gluteus maximus
	2	Gluteus medius
	3	Infraspinatus
	4	Teres major
	5	Deltoid
	6	Trapezius
	7	Biceps brachii
	8	Gastrocnemius
	9	Latissimus dorsi
20	1	Buccinator
	2	Orbicularis oculi
21	1	Buccinator
22	1	Deltoid
	2	Pectoralis major
	3	Trapezius
	4	Biceps brachii
	5	Rectus abdominis
	6	Vastus lateralis
	7	Vastus medialis
	8	Sartorius
23	1	Deltoid
	2	Trapezius
	3	Pectoralis major
	4	Rectus abdominis
	5	Biceps brachii
24	1	Frontalis
25	1	Platysma
26	1	Adductor longus
27	1	Sternocleidomastoid
28	1	Orbicularis oculi
	2	Deltoid
	3	Trapezius
	4	Sternohyoid
29	1	Biceps brachii

	2	Triceps brachii
	3	Pectoralis major
	4	Rectus abdominis
	5	Rectus femoris
	6	Vastus lateralis
	7	Sartorius
	8	Latissimus dorsi
	9	Intercostal
30	1	Sternocleidomastoid
	2	Triceps brachii
	3	Deltoid
	4	Triceps brachii
31	1	Adductor longus
	2	Biceps brachii
	3	Triceps brachii
	4	Vastus lateralis
	5	Sternocleidomastoid
	6	Diaphragm
	7	Gastrocnemius
32	1	Trapezius
	2	Infraspinatus
	3	Teres major
	4	Deltoid
	5	Supraspinatus
	6	Erector spinae group (consists of three groups of muscles iliocostalis, longissimus, and spinalis).
33	1	Gracilis
	2	Gastrocnemius
	3	Sartorius
	4	Vastus medialis
	5	Rectus femoris
34	1	Rectus femoris
	2	Vastus medialis
	3	Vastus lateralis
	4	Sartorius
	5	Gastrocnemius
35	1	Deltoid
	2	Infraspinatus
	3	Teres major

	4	Latissimus dorsi
	5	Trapezius
	6	Brachialis
36	1	Gastrocnemius
	2	Soleus
37	1	Infraspinatus
	2	Gluteus medius
	3	Gluteus maximus
	4	Trapezius
	5 (BLACK)	Rhomboideus
	5 (RED)	Vastus lateralis
38	1	Gluteus maximus
	2	Biceps femoris
	3	Semitendinosus
	4	Vastus lateralis
	5	Semimembranosus
	6	Gastrocnemius
	7	Soleus
39	1	Orbicular oris
40	1	Sartorius
	2	Sternocleidomastoid
	3	Trapezius
	4	Biceps brachii
	5	Rectus abdominis
	6	Brachioradialis
	7	Pectoralis major
	8	Triceps brachii
41	1	Teres major
	2	Infraspinatus
	3	Trapezius
	4	Deltoid
	5	Brachioradialis
	6	Triceps brachii
42	1	Triceps brachii (long head)
	2	Intercostal
	3	Biceps brachii
	4	Pectoralis major
	5	Trapezius

		6	Latissimus dorsi
		7	Brachioradialis
		8	Deltoid
		9	Masseter
43		1	Semimembranosus
		2	Semitendinosus
		3	Vastus lateralis
		4	Biceps femoris
		5	Gluteus maximus
		6	Latissimus dorsi
		7	Infraspinatus
		8	Teres major
		9	Triceps brachii (long and lateral heads)
		10	Deltoid
		11	Biceps brachii
		12	Trapezius
		13	Supraspinatus
		14	Erector spinae group
44		1	Biceps femoris
		2	Vastus lateralis
		3	Semitendinosus
		4	Biceps brachii
		5	Triceps brachii (lateral head)
		6	Triceps brachii (long head)
		7	Brachioradialis
		8	Gastrocnemius
45		1	Orbicularis oris
		2	Orbicularis oculi
46		1	Sartorius
		2	Vastus medialis
		3	Rectus femoris
		4	Adductor longus
		5	Vastus lateralis
47		1	Sartorius
		2	Adductor longus
		3	Gracilis
		4	Serratus anterior
		5	Rectus femoris

	6	Vastus lateralis
	7	Biceps brachii
	8	Triceps brachii
	9	Masseter

HUMAN SKELETAL MUSCLES
(PLASTIC MODELS)

Picture #	Question #	answers
01	1	Deltoid
	2	Trapezius
	3	Pectoralis major
	4	Pectoralis minor
	5	Rectus abdominis
	6	Internal intercostal
02	1	Temporalis
	2	Trapezius
	3	Deltoid
	4	Latissimus dorsi
	5	Gluteus maximus
	6	Triceps brachii
	7	Biceps brachii
03	1	Serratus anterior
	2	External intercostal
	3	Pectoralis minor
04	1	Deltoid
	2	Teres minor
	3	Teres major
	4	Serratus anterior
	5	Internal intercostal muscle
05	1	Frontalis of epicranius
	2	Orbicularis oculi
	3	Orbicularis oris
	4	Zygomatic
06	1	Trapezius
	2	Supraspinatus
	3	Infraspinatus
	4	Teres major
	5	Deltoid
	6	Teres minor
07	1	Tensor fasciae latae
	2	Sartorius
	3	Rectus femoris
	4	Vastus lateralis

	5	Vastus medialis
	6	Iliotibial tract
08	1	Tensor fasciae latae
	2	Gluteus maximus
	3	Vastus lateralis
	4	Biceps femoris (long head)
	5	Soleus
	6	Gastrocnemius
	7	Peroneus longus
	8	Iliotibial tract (extending down from tensor fasciae latae and covering part of vastus lateralis
	9	Calcaneal (Achilles) tendon
09	1	Vastus medialis
	2	Sartorius
	3	Adductor longus
	4	Gastrocnemius
	5	Soleus
	6	Pectineus
10	1	Gluteus maximus
	2	Biceps femoris
	3	Semitendinosus
	4	Semimembranosus
	5	Gastrocnemius
	6	Soleus
	7	Gracilis
11	1	Gluteus maximus
	2	Biceps femoris
	3	Semitendinosus
	4	Tensor fasciae latae
	5	Semimembranosus
	6	Gracilis
	7	Adductor magnus
	8	Gastrocnemius
12	1	Frontalis of epicranius
	2	Temporalis
	3	Orbicularis oculi
	4	Orbicularis oris
	5	Masseter
	6	Buccinator

	7	Sternocleidomastoid
	8	Zygomatic major
	9	Trapezius
13	1	Gracilis
	2	Sartorius
	3	Rectus femoris
	4	Vastus medialis
	5	Vastus lateralis
	6	Tensor fasciae latae
	7	Psoas major
14	1	Occipitalis
	2	Trapezius
	3	Splenius capitis
	4	Sternocleidomastoid
15	1	Gluteus maximus
	2	Gluteus medius
	3	Biceps femoris
	4	Semitendinosus
	5	Semimembranosus
	6	Adductor magnus
	7	Gracilis
	8	Gastrocnemius
	9	Soleus
16	1	Trapezius
	2	Occipitalis
	3	Levator scapulae
	4	Splenius
	5	Sternocleidomastoid
	6	Galea aponeurotica (epicranial aponeurosis)
17	1	digastric
	2	Mylohyoid
	3	Sternohyoid
18	1	Trapezius
	2	Deltoid
	3	Triceps brachii
	4	Latissimus dorsi
	5	Gluteus maximus
	6	Gluteus minimus

	7	Erector spinae (part of iliocostalis thoracic muscle)
	8	Deltoid
	9	Sciatic nerve
19	1	Supraspinatus
	2	Infraspinatus
	3	Teres major
	4	Teres minor
	5	Deltoid
20	1	Supraspinatus
	2	Infraspinatus
	3	Teres major
	4	Spine of scapula
	5	Acromion of scapula
	6	Clavicle
21	1	Supraspinatus
	2	Infraspinatus
	3	Teres major
	4	Deltoid
	5	Teres minor
22	1	Gluteus maximus
	2	Gluteus minimus
	3	Biceps femoris
	4	Sciatic nerve
23	1	Clavicle
	2	Supraspinatus
	3	Deltoid
	4	Infraspinatus
	5	Teres minor
	6	Teres major
	7	Triceps brachii (long head0
	8	Triceps brachii (lateral head)
	9	Brachialis
	10	Biceps brachii
	11	Brachioradialis
	12	Extensor carpi radialis longus
	13	Common tendon insertion of triceps brachii into olecranon process of ulna
24	1	Subscapularis
	2	Deltoid

	3	Biceps brachii
	3A	Short head of biceps brachii
	3B	Long head of biceps brachii
	4	Coracobrachialis
	5	Triceps brachii (long head)
	6	Brachialis
	7	Median nerve
25	1	Supraspinatus
	2	Deltoid
	3	Biceps brachii (long head)
	4	Brachialis
	5	Triceps brachii (lateral head)
	6	Triceps brachii (long head)
	7	Teres major
	8	Brachioradialis

MUSCLE IIISTOLOGY

Picture #	Question #	answers
01	1	Skeletal muscle fiber
	2	Endomysium
	3	Perimysium
02	1	Skeletal muscle
03	1	Peripheral nuclei of skeletal muscle
04	1	Smooth muscle
05	1	Cardiac muscle
	2	Intercalated disc
06	1	Cardiac muscle
	2	Intercalated disc
07	1	Smooth muscle
	2	Nucleus of smooth muscle fiber

NERVOUS SYSTEM
(NERVE CELLS)

Picture #	Question #	answers
01	1	Cell body (soma or perikaryon)
	2	Dendrites
	3	Axon
02	1	Dendrite
	2	Synaptic end bulbs (axon terminal) which contain neurotransmitters
	3	Axon
	4	Axon terminals (telodendria)
	5	Myelin sheath
03	1	Axon (axon cylinder)
	2	Myelin sheath
	3	Endoneurium
	4	Chromatophilic substance (Nissl bodies)
	5	Axon hillock
	6	Neurofibrils
04	1	Dendrite
	2	Synaptic end bulbs
	3	Axon terminals (telodendria)
	4	Axon hillock
	5	Nucleus

		6	Neurofibrils
05		1	Myelin sheath of neurolemmocyte
		2	Axon (axon cylinder)
		3	Endoneurium
		4	Neurolemma of neurolemmocyte
		5	Nucleus of neurolemmocyte
		6	Neurofibral node (node of Ranvier)
06		1	Axon (axon cylinder) containing neurofibrils within axoplasm
		2	Myelin sheath of neurolemmocyte
		3	Neurolemma of neurolemmocyte
		4	Endoneurium
07		1	Axon hillock
		2	Dendrites
		3	Synaptic end bulbs
		4	Axon terminals (Telodendria)
		5	Nucleus
		6	Chromatophilic substance (Nissl bodies)
		7	Axon
08		1	Nucleus of neurolemmocyte (Schwann cell)
		2	Myelin sheath of neurolemmocyte
		3	Axon (axon cylinder)
		4	Neurofibral node (node of Ranvier)
		5	Endoneurium
		6	Neurolemma of neurolemmocyte (Schwann cell)
09		1	Dendrite projections
		2	Synaptic end bulbs (synaptic knobs)
		3	Axon terminals (telodendria)
10		1	Axon
		2	Dendrite
		3	Synaptic cleft
		4	Presynaptic neuron
		5	Postsynaptic neuron
11		1	G
		2	A
		3	D
		4	F
		5	B
		6	E

	7	C
	8	Multipolar neuron
12	1	Cell body (soma or perikaryon)
	2	Nucleus
	3	Dendrites
	4	Neurolemma of neurolemmocyte (Schwann cell)
	5	Neurofibral node (node of Ranvier)
	6	Nerve fascicle
	7	Axon terminal of motor neuron
	8	Terminal cistern of sarcoplasmic reticulum within skeletal muscle fiber
	9	Axon
	10	Skeletal muscle fiber
13	1	Axon hillock
	2	Axon
	3	Synaptic end bulb (synaptic knob) that contains neurotransmitter.
	4	Axon terminals (telodendria)
	5	Axon (axolemma of axon)
	6	Cytoplasm of neurolemmocyte (Schwann cell)
	7	Myelin sheath
	8	Myelin sheath
	9	Neurofibral node (node of Ranvier)
	10	Neurolemma of neurolemmocyte (sheath of Schwann)
14	1	Nucleus
	2	Nucleolus
	3	Golgi complex
	4	Mitochondria
	5	Smooth endoplasmic reticulum
	6	Lysosome
	7	Secretory vesicle formed from Golgi complex
	8	Rough endoplasmic reticulum (ER plus ribosomes)
	9	Neurofibrils
	10	Dendrite
	11	Synaptic end bulb
	12	Axon terminals (telodendria)
15	1	Synaptic end bulbs (Synaptic end knobs)
	2	Schwann cell
	3	Myelin sheath
	4	Axon terminals (telodendria)

Picture #	Question #	answers
	4	Axon
16	1	Nissl Bodies
	2	Neurofibrils
	3	Axon hillock
	4	Dendrite
17	1	Nucleus of Schwann cell
	2	Endoneurium
	3	Synaptic end bulbs (Synaptic end knobs)

SHEEP BRAIN DISSECTIONS

Picture #	Question #	answers
01	1	Dura mater
	2	Gyri of cortex of cerebrum
02	1	Frontal lobe
	2	Parietal lobe
	3	Occipital lobe
	4	Corpus callosum
	5	Fornix
	6	Intermediate mass of thalamus
	7	Optic chiasma
	8	Pituitary gland
	9	Cerebral peduncle
03	1	Occipital lobe
	2	Parietal lobe
	3	Folia of cerebellum
	4	Frontal lobe
	5	Longitudinal fissure separating left and right cerebral hemispheres
	6	Transverse fissure separating cerebrum from cerebellum
	7	Spinal cord
04	1	Longitudinal fissure
	2	Gyrus of cortex
	3	Sulcus of cortex
05	1	Superior colliculi of corpora quadrigemina
	2	Occipital lobe of cerebral hemisphere
06	1	Septum pellucidum
	2	Fornix

	3	Pineal body
	4	Pons
	5	Medulla oblongata
	6	Spinal cord
	7	Arbor vitae of cerebellum
	8	Cerebellum
	9	Superior colliculi of corpora quadrigemina
07	1	Temporal lobe
	2	Frontal lobe
	3	Parietal lobe
	4	Cerebellum
	5	Olfactory bulb
	6	Optic chiasma (optic nerve)
	7	Pons
	8	Medulla oblongata
	9	Spinal cord
	10	Transverse fissure
	11	Central sulcus (Fissure of Rolando)
	12	Lateral sulcus (Fissure of Sylvius)
08	1	Pineal body
	2	Superior colliculi of corpora quadrigemina
	3	Inferior colliculi of corpora quadrigemina
09	1	Corpus callosum
	2	Fornix
	3	Intermediate mass of thalamus
	4	Optic chiasma
	5	Hypothalamus
	6	Mammillary body
	7	Pineal body
	8	Superior colliculi of corpora quadrigemina
	9	Cerebral peduncle
	10	Pons
	11	Medulla oblongata
	12	Spinal cord
	13	Inferior colliculi of corpora quadrigemina
	14	Lateral ventricle which contains cerebral spinal fluid (csf)
10	1	Pineal body
	2	Superior colliculi of corpora quadrigemina
	3	Cerebellum

	4	Longitudinal fissure
	5	Gyrus of cortex
11	1	Mammillary body
	2	Hypothalamus
	3	Fourth ventricle
12	1	Pituitary gland
	2	Optic chiasma (optic nerves cross)
	3	Olfactory bulb (associated with smell)
	4	Olfactory nerve (cranial nerve I)
	5	Optic nerve (cranial nerve II)
	6	Trigeminal nerve (cranial nerve V)
	7	Medulla oblongata
	8	Infundibulum
13	1	Septum pellucidum
	2	Third ventricle (contains csf)
14	1	Olfactory bulb
	2	Mammillary body
	3	Cerebral peduncle
	4	Oculomotor nerve (cranial nerve III)
	5	Pons
	6	Infundibulum
	7	Temporal lobe
15	1	Optic chiasma
	2	Mammillary body
	3	Cerebral peduncle
	4	Pons
	5	Optic nerve (cranial nerve II)
	6	Infundibulum
	7	Optic tract
16	1	Longitudinal fissure
	2	Corpus callosum
	3	Lateral ventricle which contains csf
	4	Fornix
	5	Thalamus
	6	Pituitary gland
	7	Infundibulum
	8	Third ventricle
17	1	Intermediate mass of thalamus
	2	Pineal body

	3	Superior colliculi of corpora quadrigemina
	4	Inferior colliculi of corpora quadrigemina
	5	Third ventricle
	6	Optic chiasma
18	1	Fourth ventricle
	2	Superior colliculi of corpora quadrigemina
	3	Pineal body
	4	Intermediate mass of thalamus
	5	Optic chiasma
	6	Pituitary gland
	7	Cerebral peduncle
	8	Pons
	9	Medulla oblongata
	10	Mammillary body
19	1	Optic chiasma
	2	Intermediate mass of thalamus
	3	Superior colliculi of corpora quadrigemina
	4	Inferior colliculi of corpora quadrigemina
	5	Hypothalamus
	6	Mammillary body
	7	Cerebral peduncle
	8	Pons
	9	Medullar oblongata
	10	Corpus callosum
	11	Septum pellucidum
	12	Fornix
	13	Olfactory bulb
	14	Cortex of right cerebrum
	15	arachnoid

HUMAN BRAIN
MODELS

Picture #	Question #	answers
01	1	Gyrus of right cortex of cerebrum
	2	Sulcus
	3	Frontal
	4	Temporal
	5	Occipital
	6	Parietal

	7	Cerebellum
02	1	Olfactory bulb
	2	Optic nerve (cranial nerve II)
	3	Pons
	4	Abducens nerve (cranial nerve VI)
	5	Cerebellum
	6	Hypoglossal (cranial nerve XII)
	7	Medulla oblongata
	8	Trigeminal (cranial nerve V)
03	1	Central sulcus (Fissure of Rolando)
	2	Lateral sulcus (Fissure of Sylvius)
	3	Frontal lobe
	4	Temporal lobe
	5	Parietal lobe
	6	Occipital lobe
	7	Cerebellum
	8	Sulci on cortex of cerebrum
	9	Gyri on cortex of cerebrum
04	1	Broca's area (speech)
	2	Gustatory area (taste)
	3	Auditory area (hearing)
05	1	Pons
	2	Medulla oblongata
	3	Cerebellum
	4	Olfactory nerve (cranial nerve I)
06	1	Prefrontal cortex (solving complex, multi-task problems, working memory for object-recall, personality)
	2	Frontal lobe (control skeletal muscle contraction)
	3	Temporal lobe (hearing and taste)
	4	Parietal lobe (somatosensory: texture, temperature, pressure, shape, etc.)
	5	Occipital lobe (vision: color, form, movement)
	6	Cerebellum (provide smooth skeletal muscle contraction, coordinated movement, balance)
07	1	Frontal lobe
	2	Gyrus of cortex
	3	Occipital lobe
	4	Frontal lobe
	5	Sulcus on cortex
	6	Corpus callosum
	7	Fornix

	8	Septum pellucidum
	9	Pons
	10	Midbrain
	11	Medulla oblongata
	12	Cerebellum
	13	Hypothalamus
08	1	Corpus callosum
	2	Fornix
	3	Intermediate mass of thalamus
	4	Hypothalamus
	5	Corpora quadrigemina of midbrain
	6	Pineal body (part of epithalamus)
	7	Midbrain
	8	Pons
	9	Fourth ventricle
	10	Mammillary body
09	1	Superior sagittal sinus
	2.	Dura mater
	3	Arachnoid
	4	Subarachnoid space
	5	Pia mater
	6	Pituitary gland
10	1	Longitudinal fissure
	2	Gyrus of cortex of left hemispheres
	3	Sulcus of cortex of left hemispheres
	4	Occipital lobe
	5	cerebellum

BRAIN STEM MODEL

Picture #	Question #	answers
01	1	Thalamus
	2	Superior colliculus of corpora quadrigemina
	3	Inferior colliculus of corpora quadrigemina
	4	Pineal gland
	5	Pons
	6	Medulla oblongata
02	1	Thalamus
	2	Pons
	3	Optic nerves

	4	Cerebral peduncle
	5	Choroid plexus of third ventricle
	6	Medulla oblongata
03	1	Intermediate mass of thalamus
	2	Hypothalamus
	3	Superior colliculus of corpora quadrigemina
	4	Inferior colliculus of corpora quadrigemina
	5	Midbrain
	6	Pons
	7	Medulla oblongata
	8	Mammillary body
	9	Optic chiasma
04	1	Optic nerve
	2	Cerebral peduncle
	3	Pons
	4	Medulla oblongata
	5	Abducens nerve (cranial nerve VI)

BRAIN VENTRICLE
MODELS

Picture #	Question #	answers
01	1	Lateral ventricles
	2	Third ventricle
	3	Interventricular foramen
	4	Cerebral aqueduct
	5	Fourth ventricle
02	1	Lateral ventricle
	2	Third ventricle
	3	Cerebral aqueduct
	4	Central canal of spinal cord
03	1	Lateral ventricles
	2	Third ventricle
	3	Cerebral aqueduct
	4	Interventricular foramen
04	1	Lateral ventricles
	2	Fourth ventricle
	3	Cerebral aqueduct
	4	Interventricular foramen

Picture #	Question #	answers
01	1	White matter
	2	Ventral (anterior) medial fissure
	3	Ventral (anterior) horn of gray matter
	4	Dorsal (posterior) horn of gray matter
	5	Dorsal (posterior) root ganglia
	6	Ventral (anterior) root
	7	Motor (efferent) nerve
	8	Dorsal ramus
	9	Spinal nerve
	10	Sensory (afferent) nerve
	11	Denticulate ligament
02	1	Dura mater
	2	Arachnoid mater
	3	Pia mater
	4	Epidural space
	5	Subdural space
	6	Subarachnoid space
03	1	Lateral horn of gray matter
	2	Gray commissure
	3	Central canal
	4	Cerebral spinal fluid (csf)
04	1	Body of cervical vertebra
	2	Dorsal root ganglia
	3	Dorsal ramus
	4	Ventral ramus
	5	Rami communicantes
	6	Sympathetic ganglion
	7	Superior articular process of cervical vertebra
	8	Motor (efferent) nerve or rootlets
	9	Sensory (afferent) nerve
05	1	Ventral (anterior) horn of gray matter
	2	Dorsal (posterior) horn of gray matter
	3	Gray commissure
	4	Central canal containing cerebral spinal fluid
	5	Ventral (anterior) medial fissure
	6	Sensory (afferent) nerve
06	1	White matter composed of myelinated and unmyelinated nerve fibers arranged into three white columns or funiculi.

		2	Dorsal (posterior) horn of gray matter
		3	Ventral (anterior) horn of gray matter
		4	Gray commissure
		5	Central canal
		6	Dorsal root ganglia
		7	Unipolar sensory (afferent) neuron
		8	Multipolar motor (efferent) neuron
		9	Spinal nerve
		10	Ventral (anterior) medial fissure
07			
08		1	Temporal lobe
		2	Frontal lobe
		3	Parietal lobe
		4	Occipital lobe
		5	Cerebellum
		6	Cervical enlargement
		7	Lumbar enlargement
		8	Conus medullaris
		9	Cauda equina
		10	Filum terminale
09		1	Cervical plexus
		2	Phrenic nerve
		3	Brachial plexus
		4	Cervical enlargement
		5	Lateral sulcus (Fissure of Sylvius)
		6	Central sulcus (Fissure of Rolando)
10		1	Pia mater
		2	Arachnoid
		3	Dura mater
		4	Subarachnoid space containing csf
		5	Subdural space
		6	Epidural space (contains adipose tissue)
11		1	Conus medullaris
		2	Lumbar plexus
		3	Cauda equina
		4	Sacral plexus
		5	Filum terminale
		6	Sciatic nerve forming from sacral nerve plexus
12		1	Cervical plexus (located between C1 C5)

	2	Brachial plexus (located between C5-T1)
	3	Lumbar plexus (located between L1- L4)
	4	Sacral plexus (located between L4 –S4)
	5	Cervical enlargement (extends from C4 – T1)
	6	Lumbar enlargement (extends from T9 – T12)
	7	Conus medullaris (located between first and second lumbar vertebra)
	8	Cauda equina, meaning "horse's tail" (collective roots of nerves)
	9	Coccyx bones
	10	Filum terminale (extension of pia matter that extends inferiorly and anchors the spinal cord to the coccyx)
	11	Phrenic nerve
	12	Thoracic nerves
	13	Femoral nerve
	14	Sciatic nerve
13	1	Cervical enlargement
	2	Anterior (ventral) median sulcus
	3	Cervical part of sympathetic ganglia
	4	Cervical plexus (extends from C1-C4)
	5	Phrenic nerve coming off cervical plexus
	6	Brachial plexus (extends from C5 – T1)
	7	Sympathetic ganglia (Chain ganglia)
14	1	Thoracic nerve
	2	Conus medullaris(located between first and second lumbar vertebra)
	3	Cauda equina, meaning "horse's tail" (collective roots of nerves)
	4	Filum terminale (extension of pia matter that extends inferiorly and anchors the spinal cord to the coccyx)
	5	Sympathetic ganglia
15	1	Conus medullaris
	2	Cauda equina
	3	Filum terminale
	4	Lumbar plexus
	5	Sacral plexus
	6	Femoral nerve
	7	Sciatic nerve
	8	Sympathetic ganglion in pelvic region

NERVOUS HISTOLOGY

Picture #	Question #	answers
01	1	Nervous tissue
	2	Cell body of neuron

		3	Neuroglia cells
02		1	Central canal
		2	Ventral medial fissure
		3	Dorsal (posterior) horn
		4	Ventral (anterior) horn
		5	White matter of spinal cord (posterior funiculus)
03		1	Nervous tissue
		2	Neurofibrils
		3	Nissl (chromatophilic substance) bodies
04		1	Neuron
		2	Axon projection
05		1	Efferent nerve of myoneural junction
		2	Efferent projection
		3	Motor end plate
		4	Skeletal muscle fiber

Picture #	Question #	answers
01	1	Sclera
	2	Iris
	3	Lens
	4	Choroid
	5	Pigmented layer of retina
	6	Neural (nervous) layer of retina
	7	Pupil
	8	Superior rectus muscle
02	1	Sclera
	2	Choroid
	3	Pigmented layer of retina
	4	Neural (nervous) layer of retina
	5	Lens
	6	Ciliary body
	7	Suspensory ligament
	8	Optic nerve (cranial nerve II)
03	1	Optic nerve (cranial nerve II)
	2	Macula lutea on retina
	3	Fovea centralis (central fovea of macula lutea)
04	1	Sclera
	2	Choroid
	3	Retina
	4	Blind spot (optic disc)
	5	Ora serrata
	6	Lens
	7	Cornea
05	1	Iris
	2	Pupil
06	1	Anterior chamber of anterior cavity filled with aqueous humor
	2	Posterior cavity containing vitreous body
07	1	Sclera
	2	Lacrimal gland
	3	Iris
	4	Pupil
	5	Superior rectus muscle
	6	Inferior rectus muscle

Picture #	Question #	answers
	7	Inferior oblique muscle
	8	Lateral rectus muscle
08	1	Superior rectus muscle
	2	Lateral rectus muscle
	3	Inferior rectus muscle
	4	Medial rectus muscle
	5	Superior oblique muscle
09	1	Pupil
	2	Cornea
	3	Iris
10	1	Optic nerve
	2	Sclera
11	1	Macula lutea with central fovea
	2	Optic disc (blind spot)
	3	Retinal blood vessel
12	1	Central fovea
	2	Optic disc (blind spot)
	3	Retinal blood vessel
13		

EAR

Picture #	Question #	answers
01	1	External auditory canal
	2	Eustachian (auditory or pharyngotympanic) tube
	3	Cochlea
	4	Semicircular canals
	5	Vestibulocochlear nerve
02	1	External ear
	2	Middle ear
	3	Internal (inner) ear
03	1	External auditory canal
	2	Eustachian (auditory or pharyngotympanic) tube
	3	Tympanic membrane
	4	Malleus (hammer)
	5	Vestibule
	6	Semicircular canal
	7	Cochlea
	8	Vestibulocochlear nerve

04	1	Stapes (stirrup)
	2	Vestibule
	3	Ampullae of semicircular canal
	4	Semicircular canal
	5	Cochlear
	6	Vestibulocochlear nerve
	7	Oval window
05	1	Auricle
	2	Helix
	3	Lobule
	4	Tympanic membrane (eardrum)
	5	Malleus (hammer)
	6	External auditory canal
06	1	Stapes (stirrup)
	2	Cochlea

Human Anatomy & Physiology II
Laboratory Images
For
Student Review

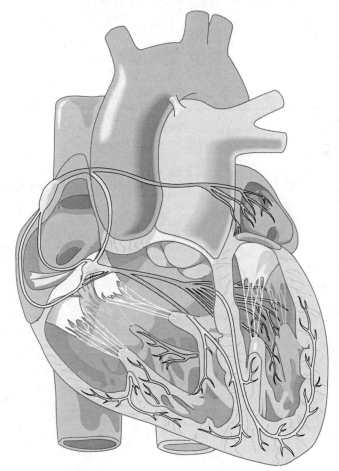

Question and Answer **Quick Find** Index
A & P II
Type in the Quick Find Word and Hit Enter Twice!

Images to view	Quick Find Word	Question pages	Answer pages	Images to view	Quick Find Word	Question pages	Answer pages
Endocrine histology	**Endocrine hist**	144-146	190-192	Digestive histology	**Digestivehist**	175	220-221
Endocrine models	**Endocrine model**	144	190	Reproductive (male) models	**Male**	180-182	226-228
				Reproductive (male) histology	**Male**	183	229
Blood cell histology	**Bloodcellhist**	147	193	Reproductive (male) dissection	**Maledissect**	182-183	228-229
Blood cell models	**Blood cell model**	146	192	Reproductive (female) models	**Female**	183-187	229-233
Blood vessel models	**Bloodvesselmodel**	154-159	200-205	Reproductive (female) histology	**Femalehist**	187	233-234
Blood vessel histology	**Bloodvesselhist**	159-160	205	Urinary models	**Urinarymodel**	176-179	222-225
				Urinary histology	**Urinaryhist**	180	226
Heart (human) models	**Heartmodel**	148-152	194-198	Urinary dissections	**Urinarydiss**	179-180	
Sheep heart dissections	**Sheepheart**	152-154					
Respiratory models	**Respmodel**	161-168	205-213				
Respiratory histology	**Resphist**	169	214				
Respiratory Dissections	**Respdis**	168	214				
Digestive models	**Digestivemodel**	169-174	215-220				

ENDOCRINE SYSTEM
MODELS
Type **ENDOCRINE MODELS** in white space in tool bar to bring up these images

Picture #	Question #	Questions
01	1	Identify the specific gland on the torso numbered 1.
02	1	Identify the specific gland on the torso numbered 1.
	2	Identify the specific gland on the torso numbered 2.
03	1	Identify the specific gland on the torso numbered 1.
	2	Identify the specific gland on the torso numbered 2.
04	1	Identify the specific structure on the ovary model numbered 1.
	2	Identify the specific structure on the ovary model numbered 2.
	3	Identify the specific structure on the ovary model numbered 3.
	4	Identify the specific structure on the ovary model numbered 4.
	5	Identify the specific structure on the ovary model numbered 5.
	6	Identify the specific structure on the ovary model numbered 6.
	7	Identify the specific structure on the ovary model numbered 7.
	8	Identify the layer on the ovary model numbered 8.
05	1	Identify the specific gland numbered 1.
	2	Identify the part of the gland numbered 2.
06	1	Identify the specific gland numbered 1.
	2	Identify the specific gland numbered 2.

ENDOCRINE HISTOLOGY
Type **ENDOCRINE HIST** in white space in tool bar to bring up these images

Picture #	Question #	Questions
01	1	Identify the gland lettered "A"
	2	Identify the specific part numbered 2.
	3.	Identify the specific cells numbered 3.
	4.	What is the function of the cells numbered 3?
02	1	Identify the gland lettered "B"
	2	Identify the specific gland numbered 2.
	3	List the hormones produced in the gland numbered 2.
	4	Identify the specific gland numbered 4.
	5	What hormones are produced in the gland numbered 4?
03	1	Identify the specific gland lettered "A".
	2	Identify the specific gland lettered "B".
04	1.	Identify the specific gland lettered "D"
	2	Identify the specific part numbered 2.

	3	Identify the specific part numbered 3.
	4	Identify the specific part numbered 4.
	5	Identify the specific gland lettered "E".
	6	Identify the specific structure numbered 6.
05	1	Identify the specific gland lettered "F".
	2	Identify the specific part numbered 2.
	3	List the hormones produced in the part numbered 2.
06	1.	Identify the specific gland lettered "G".
	2	Identify the specific gland lettered "H".
07	1	Identify the entire oval shaped structure numbered 1.
	2	Identify the reddish material numbered 2.
	3	Identify the specific cells (blue) numbered 3.
08	1	Identify the specific gland lettered "I"
	2	Identify the specific yellowish structure numbered 2.
09	1	Identify the specific gland lettered "J".
	2	Identify the specific structure numbered 2.
	3	Identify the specific structure numbered 3.
	4	Identify the specific structure (circled in black) numbered 4.
	5	Identify the whitish area numbered 5.
	6	Identify the specific structure numbered 6.
10		THERE IS NO IMAGE NUMBERED 10 AT THIS TIME
11	1	Identify the specific structure numbered 1.
	2	Identify the specific gland numbered 2.
12	1	Identify the specific gland numbered 1.
13	1	Identify the specific gland lettered "K"
14	1	Identify the gland lettered "L"
15	1	Identify this specific gland numbered 15
16	1	Identify the specific gland numbered 1.
	2	Identify the specific gland numbered 2.
17	1	Identify this specific gland.
	2	Identify the specific cell the yellow-greenish arrow is pointing to.
18	1	Identify the cells numbered 1.
	2	What substance is stored in the pinkish substance numbered 2.
19	1	Identify the gland lettered "N".
20	1	Identify the specific gland lettered "O".
	2	Identify the specific endocrine structure numbered 2.
21	1	Identify the specific gland numbered 1.
22	1	Identify the specific gland numbered 1.
	2	Identify the specific zone numbered 2.

	3	Identify the specific zone numbered 3.
	4	Identify the specific zone numbered 4.
	5	Identify the specific irregular dense connective tissue layer numbered 5
23	1	Identify the specific gland numbered 1.
	2	Identify the specific gland numbered 2.
24	1	Identify the gland numbered "P".
	2	Identify the specific part numbered 2.
	3	Identify the specific cells numbered 3.
	4	What is the function of the cells numbered 3.

THE CARDIOVASCULAR SYSTEM: BLOOD
BLOOD CELLS MODELS
Type **BLOOD CELL MODEL** in white space in tool bar to bring up these images

Picture #	Question #	Questions
01	1	Identify the specific blood cell in this picture.
	2	Identify the part on the blood cell numbered 2.
02	1	Identify the specific blood cell in this picture.
	2	Identify the specific part on the blood cell numbered 2.
	3	Identify the specific parts on the blood cell numbered 3.
03	1	Identify the specific blood cell in this picture.
	2	Identify the area on the blood cell numbered 2.
04	1	Identify the specific blood cell in this picture.
	2	Identify the specific part on the blood cell numbered 2.
	3	Identify the specific parts on the blood cell numbered 3.
05	1	Identify the specific blood cell in this picture.
	2	Identify the specific part on the blood cell numbered 2.
06	1	Identify the specific blood cell in this picture.
07	1	Identify the specific cell numbered A.
	2	Identify the specific cell numbered B.
	3	Which blood cell does not contain a nucleus?
	4	Which blood cell is larger?
08	1	Identify the specific cell in this picture.

BLOOD CELLS
HISTOLOGY
Type **BLOODCELLHIST** in white space in tool bar to bring up these images

Picture #	Question #	Questions
01	1	Identify the specific blood cell numbered 1.
	2	Identify the purple structure numbered 2.
	3	Identify the specific blood cell numbered 3.
02	1	Identify the specific blood cell numbered 1.
	2	Identify the reddish or pinkish structures numbered 2.
03	1	Identify the specific blood cell numbered 3.
04	1	Identify the specific blood cell numbered 1.
	2	Identify the structure numbered 2.
05	1	Identify the specific blood cell numbered 1.
06	1	Identify the specific blood cell numbered 1.
	2	Identify the specific blood cell numbered 2.
07	1	Identify the specific blood cell numbered 1.
	2	Identify the specific blood cell numbered 2.
08	1	Identify the specific blood cell numbered 1.
09	1	Identify the specific blood cell numbered 1.
	2	Identify the specific blood cell numbered 2.
	3	Identify the specific blood cell numbered 3.
	4	Identify the specific blood cell numbered 4.
	5	Identify the specific blood cell numbered 5.
10	1	Identify the specific blood cell numbered 1
11	1	Identify the specific blood cell numbered 1.
12	1	Identify the specific blood cell numbered 1.
13	1	Identify the specific blood cell numbered 1.
Questions 14- 17 are general knowledge questions. There are no images to identify		
	14	Which blood cell(s) are mononuclear leukocytes?
	15	Which blood cell(s) have a lobed nucleus?
	16	Which blood cell(s) are granulocytes?
	17	Which blood cell(s) are agranulocytes?

THE CARDIOVASCULAR SYSTEM: THE HEART
HUMAN HEART MODELS
Type **HEARTMODEL** in white space in tool bar to bring up these images

Picture #	Question #	Questions
01	1	Identify the cavity colored light yellow on the torso numbered 1.
02	1	Identify the area colored purple on the torso numbered 1.
03	1	Identify the specific structure on the heart numbered 1.
	2	Identify the part of the heart numbered 2.
	3	Identify the chamber of the heart numbered 3.
	4	Identify the specific structure on the heart numbered 4.
	5	Identify the blood vessel on the heart numbered 5.
	6	Identify the blood vessel on the heart numbered 6.
04	1	Identify the specific structure on the heart numbered 1.
	2	Identify the specific structure on the heart numbered 2.
	3	Identify the specific chamber on the heart numbered 3.
	4	Identify the part of the heart numbered 4.
	5	Identify the blood vessel numbered 5.
	6	Identify the blood vessel numbered 6.
	7	Identify the blood vessel numbered 7.
	8	Identify the blood vessel numbered 8.
	9	Identify the blood vessel numbered 9.
	10	Identify the blood vessel numbered 10.
	11	Identify the blood vessel numbered 11.
	12	Identify the blood vessel numbered 12.
	13	Identify the structure on the heart numbered 13.
	14	Identify the blood vessel numbered 14.
05	1	Identify the structure on the heart numbered 1.
	2	Identify the structure on the heart numbered 2.
	3	Identify the chamber on the heart numbered 3.
	4	Identify the chamber on the heart numbered 4.
	5	Identify the part of the heart numbered 5.
	6	Identify the blood vessel numbered 6.
	7	Identify the blood vessel numbered 7.
	8	Identify the blood vessel numbered 8.
	9	Identify the blood vessel numbered 9.
	10	Identify the blood vessel numbered 10.
06	1	Identify the structure on the heart numbered 1.

	2	Identify the structure on the heart numbered 2.
	3	Identify the blood vessel numbered 3.
	4	Identify the blood vessel numbered 4.
	5	Identify the blood vessel numbered 5.
	6	Identify the blood vessel numbered 6.
	7	Identify the chamber of the heart numbered 7.
	8 (yellow)	Identify the chamber of the heart numbered 8 (Yellow number 8).
	8 (black)	Identify the structure on the heart numbered 8 (Black number 8).
	9	Identify the structure on the heart numbered 9.
07	1	Identify the blood vessel numbered 1.
	2	Identify the blood vessel numbered 2.
	3	Identify the blood vessel numbered 3.
	4	Identify the blood vessel numbered 4.
	5	Identify the blood vessel numbered 5.
	6	Identify the structure on the heart numbered 6.
	7	Identify the structure on the heart numbered 7.
	8	Identify the blood vessel numbered 8.
	9	Identify the blood vessel numbered 9.
	10	Identify the part of the heart numbered 10.
	11	Identify the specific blood vessel numbered 11.
	12	Identify the specific blood vessel numbered 12.
08	1	Identify the blood vessel numbered 1.
	2	Identify the blood vessel numbered 2.
	3	Identify the blood vessel numbered 3.
	4	Identify the blood vessel numbered 4.
	5	Identify the blood vessel numbered 5.
	6	Identify the blood vessel numbered 6.
	7	Identify the blood vessel numbered 7.
	8	Identify the structure on the heart numbered 8.
	9	Identify the blood vessel numbered 9.
	10	Identify the blood vessel numbered 10.
	11	Identify the blood vessel numbered 11.
09	1	Identify the blood vessel numbered 1.
	2	Identify the blood vessel numbered 2.
	3	Identify the blood vessel numbered 3.
	4	Identify the blood vessel numbered 4.
	5	Identify the specific layer of the heart numbered 5.

10	1	Identify the blood vessel numbered 1.
	2	Identify the blood vessel numbered 2.
	3	Identify the blood vessel numbered 3.
	4	Identify the blood vessel numbered 4.
	5	Identify the blood vessel numbered 5.
	6	Identify the blood vessel numbered 6.
	7	Identify the blood vessel numbered 7
	8	Identify the blood vessel numbered 8.
11	1	Identify the chamber on the heart model numbered 1.
	2	Identify the blood vessels on the heart model numbered 2.
	3	Identify the blood vessels on the heart model numbered 3.
	4	Identify the blood vessel numbered 4.
12	1	Identify the large dilated vascular area on the posterior surface of the heart numbered 1.
	2	Identify the blood vessel numbered 2.
	3	Identify the blood vessel numbered 3.
	4	Identify the blood vessel numbered 4.
	5	Identify the blood vessel numbered 5.
	6	Identify the blood vessel numbered 6.
13	1	Identify the structure numbered 1.
	2	Identify the chamber numbered 2.
	3.	Identify the blood vessel numbered 3.
	4	Identify the blood vessel numbered 4
	5	Identify the blood vessel numbered 5.
	6	Identify the blood vessel numbered 6.
	7	Identify the blood vessel numbered 7.
	8	Identify the blood vessel numbered 8.
	9	Identify the specific chamber numbered 9.
	10	Identify the structure numbered 10.
	11	Identify the white structure numbered 11.
14	1	Identify the specific chamber numbered 1.
	2	Identify the oval depression (yellow) numbered 2.
	3	Identify the muscular ridges numbered 3.
	4	Identify the blood vessel numbered 4.
	5	Identify the irregular ridges and folds of the myocardium numbered 5.
15	1	Identify the specific chamber numbered 1.
	2	Identify the specific structure numbered 2.

	3	Identify the specific structure numbered 3.
	4	Identify the specific chamber numbered 4.
	5	Identify the blood vessel numbered 5.
16	1	Identify the specific chamber numbered 1.
	2	Identify the blood vessel numbered 2.
	3	Identify the blood vessel numbered 3.
	4	Identify the specific structure numbered 4.
	5	Identify the structure numbered 5.
	6	Identify the raised structure numbered 6.
	7	Identify the irregular surface of ridges and folds numbered 7.
	8	Identify the blood vessel numbered 8.
	9	Identify the blood vessel numbered 9
	10	Identify the white structure numbered 10.
	11	Identify the blood vessel numbered 11.
	12	Identify the blood vessel numbered 12.
	13	Identify the blood vessel numbered 13.
	14	Identify the internal muscular ridges numbered 14.
17	1	Identify the specific structure numbered 1.
	2	Identify the blood vessel numbered 2.
	3	Identify the specific chamber numbered 3.
18	1	Identify the specific chamber numbered 1.
	2	Identify the blood vessel numbered 2.
	3	Identify the ridges numbered 3.
	4	Identify the specific structure numbered 4.
	5	Identify the string like structures numbered 5.
	6	Identify the structure within the heart numbered 6.
	7	Identify the specific chamber numbered 7.
	8	Identify the specific structure numbered 8.
	9	Identify the structures numbered 9.
	10	Identify the raised structure numbered 10.
	11	Identify the anatomical part of the heart numbered 11.
	12	Identify the specific structure (white in color) numbered 12.
19	1	Identify the structure located in the right atrium numbered 1.
	2	Identify the oval depression numbered 2.
	3	Identify the structure located in the right atrium numbered 3.
	4	Identify the specific structure numbered 4.
	5	Identify the specific structure numbered 5.

	6	Identify the blood vessel numbered 6.
	7	Identify the blood vessel numbered 7.
	8	Identify the structure numbered 8.
	9	Identify the string like structures numbered 9.
	10	Identify the structure located in the ventricle numbered 10.
20	1	Identify the blood vessel numbered 1.
	2	Identify the blood vessel numbered 2.
	3	Identify the blood vessel numbered 3.
	4	Identify the blood vessel numbered 4.
	5	Identify the blood vessel numbered 5.
	6	Identify the blood vessel numbered 6.
	7	Identify the blood vessel numbered 7.
21	1	Identify the valve numbered 1.
	2	Identify the specific structure numbered 2.
	3	Identify the specific structure numbered 3.
	4	Identify the structure numbered 4.
	5	Identify the structure numbered 5.

SHEEP HEART
DISSECTIONS
Type **SHEEPHEART** in white space in tool bar to bring up these images

Picture #	Question #	Questions
01	1	Identify the specific structure on the sheep heart numbered 1.
	2	Identify the specific structure on the sheep heart numbered 2.
	3	Identify the specific chamber on the sheep heart numbered 3.
	4	Identify the specific chamber on the sheep heart numbered 4.
	5	Identify the part of the sheep heart numbered 5.
	6	Identify the blood vessel on sheep heart numbered 6.
	7	Identify the blood vessel on the sheep heart numbered 7.
02	1	Identify the specific structure on the sheep heart numbered 1.
	2	Identify the specific structure on the sheep heart numbered 2.
	3	Identify the blood vessel on the sheep heart numbered 3.
	4	Identify the specific chamber on the sheep heart numbered 4.
	5	Identify the specific chamber of the sheep heart numbered 5.
	6	Identify the groove (yellow area) on the sheep heart numbered 6.
03	1	Identify the blood vessel on the sheep heart numbered 1.
	2	Identify the blood vessel on the sheep heart numbered 2.

	3	Identify the blood vessel on the sheep heart numbered 3.
	4	Identify the specific structure on the sheep heart numbered 4.
	5	Identify the specific structure on the sheep heart numbered 5.
04	1	Identify the specific structure on the sheep heart numbered 1.
	2	Identify the blood vessel on the sheep heart numbered 2.
05	1	Identify the specific structure on the sheep heart numbered 1.
	2	Identify the structure on the sheep heart numbered 2.
06	1	Identify the specific layer of the sheep heart numbered 1.
	2	Identify the layer of the sheep heart numbered 2.
	3	Identify the layer of the sheep heart numbered 3.
07	1	Identify the specific layer of the sheep heart numbered 1.
	2	Identify the specific layer of the sheep heart numbered 2.
	3	Identify the specific layer of the sheep heart numbered 3.
	4	Identify the specific chamber of the sheep heart numbered 4.
	5	Identify the specific chamber of the sheep heart numbered 5.
08	1	Identify the blood vessel on the sheep heart numbered 1.
	2	Identify the blood vessel on the sheep heart numbered 2.
	3	Identify the blood vessel on the sheep heart numbered 3.
	4	Identify the specific structure on the sheep heart numbered 4.
09	1	Identify the blood vessel on the sheep heart numbered 1.
	2	Identify the blood vessel on the sheep heart numbered 2.
	3	Identify the specific structure on the sheep heart numbered 3.
10	1	Identify the specific space on the sheep heart numbered 1.
	2	Identify the specific structure on the sheep heart numbered 2.
	3	Identify the cord like structures on the sheep heart numbered 3.
	4	Identify the specific structure on the sheep heart numbered 4.
	5	Identify the specific chamber on the sheep heart numbered 5.
	6	Identify the specific layer on the sheep heart numbered 6.
11	1	Identify the specific structure on the sheep heart numbered 1.
	2	Identify the specific space on the sheep heart numbered 2.
	3	Identify the specific space on the sheep heart numbered 3.
	4	Identify the blood vessel on the sheep heart numbered 4.
	5	Identify the blood vessel on the sheep heart numbered 5.
	6	Identify the blood vessel on the sheep heart numbered 6.
	7	Identify the structure on the sheep heart numbered 7.
	8	Identify the specific space on the sheep heart numbered 8.

	9	Identify the specific structure on the sheep heart numbered 9.
	10	Identify the cord like structures on the sheep heart numbered 10.
	11	Identify the space on the sheep heart numbered 11.
	12	Identify the raised area on the sheep heart numbered 12.
	13	Identify the specific valve on the sheep heart numbered 13.

THE CARDIOVASCULAR SYSTEM: BLOOD VESSELS (MODELS)
Type **BLOODVESSELMODEL** in white space in tool bar to bring up these images

Picture #	Question #	Questions
01	1	Identify the specific structure on the torso numbered 1.
	2	Identify the blood vessel numbered 2.
	3	Identify the blood vessel numbered 3.
	4	Identify the blood vessel numbered 4.
	5	Identify the blood vessel numbered 5.
	6	Identify the blood vessel numbered 6.
	7	Identify the blood vessel numbered 7.
	8	Identify the blood vessel numbered 8.
	9	Identify the blood vessel numbered 9.
02	1	Identify the blood vessel numbered 1.
	2	Identify the blood vessel numbered 2.
	3	Identify the blood vessel numbered 3.
	4	Identify the blood vessel numbered 4.
	5	Identify the blood vessel numbered 5.
	6	Identify the blood vessel numbered 6.
03	1	Identify the blood vessel numbered 1.
	2	Identify the blood vessel numbered 2.
	3	Identify the blood vessel numbered 3.
	4	Identify the blood vessel numbered 4.
	5	Identify the blood vessel numbered 5.
	6	Identify the blood vessel numbered 6.
	7	Identify the blood vessel numbered 7.
	8	Identify the blood vessel numbered 8.
04	1	Identify the blood vessel numbered 1.
	2	Identify the blood vessel numbered 2.
05	1	Identify the specific coronary blood vessel numbered 1.
	2	Identify the specific coronary blood vessel numbered 2.

	3	Identify the specific coronary blood vessel numbered 3.
06	1	Identify the blood vessel numbered 1.
	2	Identify the blood vessel numbered 2.
	3	Identify the blood vessel numbered 3.
	4	Identify the blood vessel numbered 4.
	5	Identify the blood vessel numbered 5.
	6	Identify the blood vessel numbered 6.
	7	Identify the blood vessel numbered 7.
	8	Identify the blood vessel numbered 8.
	9	Identify the blood vessel numbered 9.
	10	Identify the blood vessel numbered 10.
	11	Identify the red blood vessel numbered 11.
	11	Identify the blue blood vessel numbered 11.
07	1	Identify the blood vessel numbered 1.
	2	Identify the blood vessel numbered 2.
	3	Identify the blood vessel numbered 3.
	4	Identify the blood vessel numbered 4.
	5	Identify the blood vessel numbered 5.
	6	Identify the blood vessel numbered 6.
	7	Identify the blood vessel numbered 7.
	8	Identify the blood vessel numbered 8.
08	1	Identify the blood vessel on the vascular tree model numbered 1.
	2	Identify the blood vessel on the vascular tree model numbered 2.
	3	Identify the blood vessel on the vascular tree model numbered 3.
	4	Identify the blood vessel on the vascular tree model numbered 4.
	5	Identify the blood vessel on the vascular tree model numbered 5.
	6	Identify the blood vessel on the vascular tree model numbered 6.
	7	Identify the blood vessel on the vascular tree model numbered 7.
09	1	Identify the blood vessel numbered 1.
	2	Identify the blood vessel numbered 2.
	3	Identify the blood vessel numbered 3.
	4	Identify the blood vessel numbered 4.
	5	Identify the blood vessel numbered 5.
10	1	Identify the blood vessel on the vascular tree model numbered 1.
	2	Identify the blood vessel on the vascular tree model numbered 2.
	3	Identify the blood vessel on the vascular tree model numbered 3.
	4	Identify the blood vessel on the vascular tree model numbered 4.

	5	Identify the blood vessel on the vascular tree model numbered 5.
	6	Identify the blood vessel on the vascular tree model numbered 6.
	7	Identify the blood vessel on the vascular tree model numbered 7
	8	Identify the blood vessel on the vascular tree model numbered 8.
11	1	Identify the blood vessel on the vascular tree model numbered 1.
	2	Identify the blood vessel on the vascular tree model numbered 2.
	3	Identify the blood vessel on the vascular tree model numbered 3.
	4	Identify the blood vessel on the vascular tree model numbered 4.
	5	Identify the blood vessel on the vascular tree model numbered 5.
	6	Identify the blood vessel on the vascular tree model numbered 6.
12	1	Identify the blood vessel on the vascular tree model numbered 1.
	2	Identify the blood vessel on the vascular tree model numbered 2.
	3	Identify the blood vessel on the vascular tree model numbered 3.
	4	Identify the blood vessel on the vascular tree model numbered 4.
	5	Identify the blood vessel on the vascular tree model numbered 5.
	6	Identify the blood vessel on the vascular tree model numbered 6.
	7	Identify the blood vessel on the vascular tree model numbered 7.
13	1	Identify the blood vessel on the vascular tree model numbered 1.
	2	Identify the blood vessel on the vascular tree model numbered 2.
	3	Identify the blood vessel on the vascular tree model numbered 3.
	4	Identify the blood vessel on the vascular tree model numbered 4.
	5	Identify the blood vessel on the vascular tree model numbered 5.
	6	Identify the blood vessel on the vascular tree model numbered 6.
	7	Identify the blood vessel on the vascular tree model numbered 7.
	8	Identify the blood vessel on the vascular tree model numbered 8.
	9	Identify the blood vessel on the vascular tree model numbered 9.
	10	Identify the blood vessel on the vascular tree model numbered 10.
14	1	Identify the blood vessel on the vascular tree model numbered 1.
	2	Identify the blood vessel on the vascular tree model numbered 2.
	3	Identify the blood vessel on the vascular tree model numbered 3.
	4	Identify the blood vessel on the vascular tree model numbered 4.
15	1	Identify the blood vessel on the vascular tree model numbered 1.
	2	Identify the blood vessel on the vascular tree model numbered 2.
	3	Identify the blood vessel on the vascular tree model numbered 3.
	4	Identify the blood vessel on the vascular tree model numbered 4.
	5	Identify the blood vessel on the vascular tree model numbered 5.

	6	Identify the blood vessel on the vascular tree model numbered 6.
	7	Identify the blood vessel on the vascular tree model numbered 7.
	8	Identify the blood vessel on the vascular tree model numbered 8. The vessel is number in two places showing its entire length.
	9	Identify the blood vessel on the vascular tree model numbered 9.
	10	Identify the blood vessel on the vascular tree model numbered 10.
	11	Identify the blood vessel on the vascular tree model numbered 11.
	12	Identify the blood vessel on the vascular tree model numbered 12.
16	1	Identify the blood vessel on the vascular tree model numbered 1.
	2	Identify the blood vessel on the vascular tree model numbered 2.
	3	Identify the blood vessel on the vascular tree model numbered 3.
	4	Identify the blood vessel on the vascular tree model numbered 4.
	5	Identify the blood vessel on the vascular tree model numbered 5.
	6	Identify the blood vessel on the vascular tree model numbered 6.
17	1	Identify the blood vessel on the vascular tree model numbered 1.
	2	Identify the blood vessel on the vascular tree model numbered 2.
18	1	Identify the blood vessel on the vascular tree model numbered 1.
	2	Identify the blood vessel on the vascular tree model numbered 2.
	3	Identify the blood vessel on the vascular tree model numbered 3.
	4	Identify the blood vessel on the vascular tree model numbered 4.
	5	Identify the blood vessel on the vascular tree model numbered 5.
	6	Identify the blood vessel on the vascular tree model numbered 6.
	7	Identify the blood vessel on the vascular tree model numbered 7.
19	1	Identify the blood vessel on the vascular tree model numbered 1.
	2	Identify the blood vessel on the vascular tree model numbered 2.
	3	Identify the blood vessel on the vascular tree model numbered 3.
	4	Identify the blood vessel on the vascular tree model numbered 4.
	5	Identify the blood vessel on the vascular tree model numbered 5.
	6	Identify the blood vessel on the vascular tree model numbered 6.
	7	Identify the blood vessel on the vascular tree model numbered 7.
20	1	Identify the blood vessel numbered 1.
	2	Identify the blood vessel numbered 2.
	3	Identify the blood vessel numbered 3.
	4	Identify the blood vessel numbered 4.
	5	Identify the blood vessel numbered 5.
	6	Identify the blood vessel numbered 6.
	7	Identify the blood vessel numbered 7.

	8	Identify the blood vessel numbered
	9	Identify the blood vessel numbered 9.
21	1	Identify the blood vessel on the vascular tree model numbered 1.
	2	Identify the blood vessel on the vascular tree model numbered 2.
	3	Identify the blood vessel on the vascular tree model numbered 3,
	4	Identify the blood vessel on the vascular tree model numbered 4.
	5	Identify the blood vessel on the vascular tree model numbered 5.
	6	Identify the blood vessel on the vascular tree model numbered 6.
	7	Identify the blood vessel on the vascular tree model numbered 7.
	8	Identify the blood vessel on the vascular tree model numbered 8.
	9	Identify the blood vessel on the vascular tree model numbered 9.
	10	Identify the blood vessel on the vascular tree model numbered 10.
22	1	Identify the blood vessel on the vascular tree model numbered 1.
	2	Identify the blood vessel on the vascular tree model numbered 2.
	3	Identify the blood vessel on the vascular tree model numbered 3.
	4	Identify the blood vessel on the vascular tree model numbered 4.
	5	Identify the blood vessel on the vascular tree model numbered 5.
23	1	Identify the blood vessel on the vascular tree model numbered 1.
	2	Identify the blood vessel on the vascular tree model numbered 2.
	3	Identify the blood vessel on the vascular tree model numbered 3.
	4	Identify the blood vessel on the vascular tree model that is part of the cerebral arterial circle (Circle of Willis) numbered 4.
24	1	Identify the blood vessel on the vascular tree model numbered 1.
	2	Identify the blood vessel on the vascular tree model numbered 2.
	3	Identify the blood vessel on the vascular tree model numbered 3.
	4	Identify the blood vessel on the vascular tree model numbered 4.
	5	Identify the blood vessel on the vascular tree model numbered 5.
25	1	Identify the blood vessel on the torso numbered 1.
	2	Identify the blood vessel on the torso numbered 2.
	3	Identify the blood vessel on the torso numbered 3.
	4	Identify the blood vessel on the torso numbered 4.
	5	Identify the blood vessel on the torso numbered 5.
26	1	Identify the blood vessel on the torso numbered 1.
	2	Identify the blood vessel on the torso numbered 2.
	3	Identify the blood vessel on the torso numbered 3.
	4	Identify the blood vessel on the torso numbered 4.
	5	Identify the blood vessel on the torso numbered 5.

27	1	Identify the type of blood vessel on the blood vessel model labeled A
	2	Identify the type of blood vessel on the blood vessel model labeled B
	3	Identify the lining of the inner most tunica (coat) on the blood vessel model labeled 1. Name the innermost tunica (coat).
	4	Identify the blood vessel tunica (coat) on the blood vessel model labeled 2
	5	Identify the blood vessel tunica (coat) on the blood vessel model labeled 3
	6	Identify the specific structure on the blood vessel model labeled 4
28	1	Identify the lining of the inner most tunica (coat) on the blood vessel model labeled 1. Name the innermost tunica (coat).
	2	Identify the specific layer of the innermost blood vessel tunica (coat) on the blood vessel model labeled 2
	3	Identify the blood vessel tunica (coat) on the blood vessel model labeled 3
	4	Identify the specific layer of the outermost blood vessel tunica (coat) on the blood vessel model labeled 4
	5	Identify the blood vessel tunica (coat) on the blood vessel model labeled 5
29	1	Identify the type of muscle on the blood vessel model labeled 1
	2	What vein condition would show this defect?
30	1	Identify the type of blood vessel on the blood vessel model labeled A
	2	Identify the lining of the innermost blood vessel tunica (coat) on the blood vessel model labeled 1
	3	Identify the blood vessel tunica (coat) on the blood vessel model labeled 2
	4	Identify the blood vessel tunica (coat) on the blood vessel model labeled 3

THE CARDIOVASCULAR SYSTEM: BLOOD VESSELS
HISTOLOGY
Type **BLOODVESSELHIST** in white space in tool bar to bring up these images

Picture #	Question #	Questions
01	1	Identify the blood vessel numbered 1 (artery or vein)
	2	Identify the blood vessel numbered 2 (artery or vein)
	3	Identify the specific layer numbered 3.
	4	Identify the specific layer numbered 4.
02	1	Identify the blood vessel numbered 1 (artery or vein)

1. What clinical test is used to determine the percentage of red blood cells in circulation?

2. List the three different type of blood cells that are referred to as formed elements.

3. Oxygen is transported attached to what part of a hemoglobin molecule.

4. Which formed element is required for normal blood clotting?

5. Human red blood cells have what type of shape?

6. Leukocytes are classified by presence or absence of _____ and shape of _____.

7. Which white blood cell has reddish stained granules?

8. Which white blood cell is the largest in diameter?

9. Your blood type is based on which _____ are located on the red blood cell membrane.

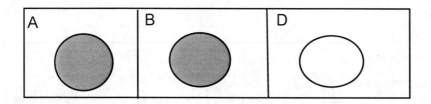

10. Determine the blood type of the following individual based on the following results. Anti - a is added to the first drop blood and agglutination occurred. Anti- b is added to the second drop of blood and agglutination occurred. Anti-d is add to the third drop of blood and no agglutination occurred. What blood type is this person?

Picture #	Question #	Questions
01	1	Identify the space numbered 1.
	2	Identify the specific bone structure numbered 2.
	3	Identify the space numbered 3.
	4	Identify the opening(s) numbered 4.
	5	Identify the area in the nose numbered 5.
	6	Identify the space numbered 6.
	7	Identify the lymphoid tissue numbered 7.
	8	Identify the space numbered 8.
	9	Identify the opening numbered 9.
	10	Identify the specific area in the nose numbered 10.
	11	Identify the specific bone numbered 11.
	12	Identify the specific bone numbered 12.
02	1	Identify the anatomical part of the lung numbered 1.
	2	Identify the anatomical part of the lung numbered 2.
	3	Identify the concave indication of the lung numbered 3.
	4	Identify the specific layer of the membrane associated with the lung "B" numbered 4.
	5	Identify the space numbered 5.
	6	Identify the specific layer of the membrane associated with the lung "B" numbered 6.
	7	Determine left or right for lung "A".
	8	Determine left or right for lung "B".
03	1	Identify the specific skeletal muscle numbered 1.
	2	Identify the specific lobe numbered 2.
	3	Identify the specific lobe numbered 3.
	4	Identify the specific lobe numbered 4.
	5	Identify the specific lobe numbered 5.
	6	Identify the specific lobe numbered 6.
	7	Identify the fissure numbered 7.
	8	Identify the fissure numbered 8.
	9	Identify the fissure numbered 9.
	9*	Identify the bone numbered 9.
04	1	Identify the specific cartilage numbered 1.
	2	Identify the specific cartilage numbered 2.

	3	Identify the specific cartilage numbered 3.
	4	Identify the specific structure numbered 4.
	5	Identify the specific structure numbered 5.
	6	Identify the specific structure numbered 6.
	7	Identify the specific structure numbered 7.
05	1	Identify the structure numbered 1.
	2	Identify the specific structure numbered 2.
	3	Identify the specific structure numbered 3.
	4	Identify the specific structure numbered 4.
	5	Identify the specific structure numbered 5.
06	1	Identify the specific cartilage numbered 1.
	2	Identify the specific cartilage numbered 2.
	3	Identify the specific structure numbered 3.
	4	Identify the specific gland numbered 4.
	5	Identify the specific structure numbered 5.
	6	Identify the specific structure numbered 6
	7	Identify the specific structure numbered 7.
	8	Identify the specific structure numbered 8.
	9	Identify the specific structure numbered 9.
07	1	Identify the specific structure numbered 1.
	2	Identify the specific structure numbered 2.
	3	Identify the specific structure numbered 3.
	4	Identify the membrane numbered 4
08	1	Identify the specific structure numbered 1.
	2	Identify the specific structure numbered 2.
	3	Identify the specific structure numbered 3.
	4	Identify the specific structure numbered 4.
	5	Identify the specific structure numbered 5.
09	1	Identify the bone numbered 1.
	2	Identify the membrane numbered 2.
	3	Identify the specific structure numbered 3.
	4	Identify the specific structure numbered 4.
	5	Identify the specific structure numbered 5.
10	1	Identify the bone numbered 1.
	2	Identify the specific cartilage numbered 2.
	3	Identify the specific cartilage numbered 3.
	4	Identify the specific cartilage numbered 4.

	5	Identify the specific cartilage numbered 5.
	6	Identify the opening colored yellow through which air passes numbered 6.
11	1	Identify the specific cartilage numbered 1.
	2	Identify the specific cartilage numbered 2.
	3	Identify the specific cartilage numbered 3.
	4	Identify the specific cartilage numbered 4.
	5	Identify the specific structure numbered 5.
	6	Identify the white structure numbered 6.
	7	Identify the specific cartilage numbered 7.
	8	Identify the structure numbered 8.
12	1	Identify the bone numbered 1.
	2	Identify the specific structure numbered 2.
	3	Identify the specific structure numbered 3.
	4	Identify the specific structure numbered 4.
	5	Identify the gland numbered 5.
	6	Identify the specific structures numbered 6.
	7	Identify the specific prominence numbered 7.
13	1	Identify the space numbered 1.
	2	Identify the space numbered 2.
	3	Identify the area in the nose numbered 3.
	4	Identify the specific structure numbered 4.
	5	Identify the space numbered 5.
	6	Identify the opening numbered 6.
	7	Identify the specific structure numbered 7.
	8	Identify the anatomical portion numbered 8.
	9	Identify the anatomical portion numbered 9.
	10	Identify the anatomical portion numbered 10.
	11	Identify the skeletal muscle structure numbered 11.
	12	Identify the specific structure numbered 12.
	13	Identify the tubular structure numbered 13.
14	1	Identify the specific structure numbered 1.
	2	Identify the specific structure numbered 2.
	3	Identify the specific structure numbered 3.
	4	Identify the specific structure numbered 4.
	5	Identify the gland numbered 5.
	6	Identify the specific structure numbered 6.
	7	Identify the specific structure numbered 7.

15	1	Identify the specific serous membrane (pink in color) numbered 1.
	2	Identify the specific serous membrane (tannish in color) numbered 2.
16	1	Identify the specific lobe numbered 1.
	2	Identify the specific lobe numbered 2.
	3	Identify the specific lobe numbered 3.
	4	Identify the specific fissure numbered 4.
	5	Identify the specific fissure numbered 5.
	6	Identify the specific organ lettered "A".
17	1	Identify the specific lobe numbered 1.
	2	Identify the specific lobe numbered 2.
	3	Identify the specific lobe numbered 3.
	4	Identify the specific fissure numbered 4.
	5	Identify the specific fissure numbered 5.
	6	Identify the concave area numbered 6.
18	1	Identify the specific fissure numbered 1.
	2	Identify the specific lobe numbered 2.
	3	Identify the specific lobe numbered 3.
	4	Identify the specific portion numbered 4.
	5	Identify the specific portion numbered 5.
	6	Identify the specific organ lettered "A".
19	1	Identify the specific structure numbered 1.
	2	Identify the specific structure numbered 2.
	3	Identify the specific fissure numbered 3.
	4	Identify the portion of this organ numbered 4.
	5	Identify the concave region of this organ numbered 5.
20	1	Identify the cartilage numbered 1.
	2	Identify the cartilage numbered 2.
	3	Identify the cartilage numbered 3.
	4	Identify the cartilage numbered 4.
	5	Identify the cartilage numbered 5.
	6	Identify the cartilage numbered 6.
21	1	Identify the cartilage numbered 1.
	2	Identify the cartilage numbered 2.
	3	Identify the cartilage numbered 3.
	4	Identify the white structure numbered 4.
	5	Identify the space (yellow arrows) numbered 5.
22	1	Identify the specific structure numbered 1.

	2	Identify the specific structure numbered 2.
	3	Identify the specific structure numbered 3.
23	1	Identify the specific structure numbered 1.
	2	Identify the specific structure numbered 2.
	3	Identify the specific structure numbered 3.
	4	Identify the specific structure numbered 4.
	5	Identify the specific structure numbered 5.
	6	Identify the specific structure numbered 6.
	7	Identify the specific structure numbered 7.
	8	Identify the specific structure numbered 8
	9	Identify the portion numbered 9.
	10	Identify the portion numbered 10.
	11.	Identify the specific organ lettered "A".
	12	Identify the specific organ lettered "B".
24	1	When the air and balloons are moving as indicated by arrows, which stage of respiration is occurring?
25	1	When the air and balloons are moving as indicated by arrows, which stage of respiration is occurring?
26	1	This picture of balloons and plastic bell jar is designed to demonstrate pulmonary ventilation. The area numbered 1 indicates which specific pressure?
	2	This picture of balloons and plastic bell jar is designed to demonstrate pulmonary ventilation. The area numbered 2 indicates which specific pressure?
	3	Based on what is happening in this demonstration, which pressure is lower, 1 or 2.
27	1.	Identify the tubular structure on the lung lobule model numbered 1. Let me give you a clue. This structure does not have cartilage.
	2	Identify the tubular structure on the lung lobule model numbered 2. Let me give you a clue. This structure does have plates of cartilage.
	3	Identify the tubular structure on the lung lobule model numbered 3. Let me give you a clue. This structure does not have cartilage.
	4	Identify the specific layer of the pleura numbered 4.
28	1	Identify the tubular structure on the lung lobule numbered 1.
	2	Identify the specific structure numbered 2.
	3	Identify the specific layer on the lung lobule model numbered 3.
29	1	Identify the specific structure on the lung lobule model numbered 1.
	2	Identify the specific layer of the pleura numbered 2.
	3	Identify the specific layer of the pleura numbered 3.

	4	Identify the specific layer of the pleura numbered 4.
	5	Identify the specific layer of the pleura numbered 5.
30	1	Identify the blood vessels on the lung lobule model numbered 1.
	2	Identify the structure on the lung lobule model numbered 2.
31	1	Identify the specific elastic cartilage on the respiratory tree model numbered 1.
	2	Identify the bone on the respiratory tree model numbered 2.
	3	Identify the membrane on the respiratory tree model numbered 3.
	4	Identify the specific cartilage on the respiratory tree model numbered 4.
	5	Identify the ligament on the respiratory tree model numbered 5.
	6	Identify the specific cartilage on the respiratory tree model numbered 6.
	7	Identify the ligament on the respiratory tree model numbered 7.
	8	Identify the skeletal muscle on the respiratory tree model numbered 8.
	9	Identify the skeletal muscle on the respiratory tree model numbered 9.
	10	Identify the gland on the respiratory tree model numbered 10.
	11	Identify the tubular structure on the respiratory tree model numbered 11.
	12	Identify the structure on the tubular structure numbered 12.
	13	Identify the specific cartilage on the respiratory tree model numbered 13, and describe its anatomical location.
	14	Identify the specific tubular structure on the respiratory tree model numbered 14.
	15	Identify the specific tubular structure on the respiratory tree model numbered 15.
	16	Identify the specific tubular structure on the respiratory tree model numbered 16.
	17	Identify the specific tubular structure on the respiratory tree model numbered 17.
	18	Identify the specific tubular structure on the respiratory tree model numbered 18.
	19	How many of the structures numbered 18 does each human lung contain?
32	1	Identify the specific elastic cartilage on the posterior view of the respiratory tree numbered 1.
	2	Identify the specific cartilage numbered 2.
	3	Identify the specific cartilage numbered 3.
	4	Identify the specific cartilage numbered 4.
	5	Identify the specific cartilage numbered 5.

	6	Identify the specific skeletal muscle numbered 6.
	7	Identify the specific gland numbered 7.
	8	Identify the tubular structure numbered 8.
	9	Identify the whitish structure numbered 9 located on the posterior surface of the tubular structure.
	10	Identify the specific tubular structures numbered 10.
	11	Identify the specific tubular structures numbered 11.
	12	Identify the specific tubular structure numbered 12.
	13	Identify the specific tubular structure numbered 13.
	14	Identify the specific tubular structure numbered 14.
33	1	Identify the specific structure on the anterior view of the respiratory tree numbered 1.
	2	Identify the specific cartilage numbered 2.
	3	Identify the specific tubular structure on the respiratory tree numbered 3.
	4	Identify the specific tubular structure on the respiratory tree numbered 4.
	5	Identify the specific tubular structure on the respiratory tree numbered 5.
	6	Identify the specific tubular structure on the respiratory tree numbered 6.
	7	Identify the specific tubular structure on the respiratory tree numbered 7.
	8	Identify the specific tubular structure on the respiratory tree numbered 8.
34	1	Identify the cartilage structure numbered 1.
	2	Identify the structure numbered 2.
	3	Identify the cartilage structure numbered 3.
	4	Identify the cartilage structure numbered 4.
	5	Identify the structure numbered 5.
	6	Identify the cartilage structure numbered 6.
	7	Identify the tubular structure numbered 7.
	8	Identify the cartilage structure numbered 8.
	9	Identify the cartilage structure numbered 9.
	10	Identify the cartilage structure numbered 10.
35	1	Identify the specific cartilage on the larynx model numbered 1.
	2	Identify the bone on the larynx model numbered 2.
	3	Identify the membrane on the larynx model numbered 3.

	4	Identify the cartilage on the larynx model numbered 4
	5	Identify the protruding portion of the cartilage on the larynx model numbered 5.
	6	Identify the ligament on the larynx model numbered 6.
	7	Identify the cartilage on the larynx model numbered 7.
	8	Identify the ligament on the larynx model numbered 8.
	9	Identify the gland on the larynx model numbered 9.
	10	Identify the structure on the model numbered 10.
36	1	Identify the specific gland (green in color) numbered 1.
	2	Identify the specific gland numbered 2.
	3	Identify the specific cartilage on the posterior view of the larynx numbered 3
	4	Identify the specific cartilage on the posterior view of the larynx numbered 4
	5	Identify the specific cartilage on the posterior view of the larynx numbered 5
	6	Identify the specific cartilage on the posterior view of the larynx numbered 6
	7	Identify the specific cartilage on the posterior view of the larynx numbered 7
	8	Identify the specific cartilage on the posterior view of the larynx numbered 8

RESPIRATORY SYSTEM
DISSECTIONS
Type **RESPDIS** white space in tool bar to bring up these images

Picture #	Question #	Questions
01	1	Identify the organ numbered 1 on the sheep pluck dissection.
	2	Identify the structure numbered 2 on the sheep pluck dissection.
	3	Identify the structure numbered 3 on the sheep pluck dissection.
	4	Identify the structure numbered 4 on the sheep pluck dissection.
	5	Identify the structure numbered 5 on the sheep pluck dissection.
02	1	Identify the specific structure numbered 1.
03	1	Identify the specific structure numbered 1.
	2	Identify the structure numbered 2.
04	1	Identify the specific structure numbered 1.

RESPIRATORY SYSTEM
HISTOLOGY
Type **resphist** space in tool bar to bring up these images

Picture #	Question #	Questions
01	1	Identify the organ numbered 1.
02	1	Identify the specific tissue numbered 1.
03	1	Identify the specific tissue numbered 1.
04	1	Identify the specific cells numbered 1
05	1	Identify the specific respiratory structure numbered 1.
	2	Identify the specific tubular respiratory structure numbered 2.
06	1	Identify the specific tubular respiratory structure numbered 1.
	2	Identify the specific respiratory structure numbered 2.
07	1	Identify the organ lettered "A".
	2	Identify the specific respiratory structure numbered 2.
08	1	Identify the organ lettered "B".
	2	Identify the specific respiratory structure numbered 2.
09	1	Identify the structure numbered 1.
	2	Identify the structure numbered 2.
10	1	Identify the structure numbered 1.

DIGESTIVE SYSTEM MODELS
Type **DIGESTIVEMODEL** space in tool bar to bring up these images

Picture #	Question #	Questions
01	1	Identify the structure numbered 1.
	2	Identify the structure numbered 2.
	3	Identify the lymphoid tissue numbered 3.
	4	Identify the arch in the oral cavity numbered 4.
	5	Identify the arch in the oral cavity numbered 5.
	6	Identify the lymphoid tissue numbered 6.
	7	Identify the skeletal muscle structure numbered 7.
	8	Identify the structure numbered 8.
	9	Identify the space numbered 9.
02	1	Identify the gland numbered 1.
	2	Identify the duct numbered 2.
	3	Identify the gland numbered 3.

03	1	Identify the gland numbered 1.
	2	Identify the duct numbered 2.
04	1	Identify the specific visceral peritoneum fold numbered 1.
	2	Identify the longitudinal bands of muscle (white in color) numbered 2.
	3	Identify the pouches (puckers) numbered 3.
05	1	Identify the structure numbered 1.
	2	Identify the specific gland numbered 2.
	3	Identify the specific gland numbered 3.
06	1	Identify the papillae (peg-like projection) numbered 1.
	2	Identify the reddish papillae numbered 2.
	3	Identify the whitish papillae numbered 3.
	4	Identify the lymphoid tissue numbered 4.
07	1	Identify the teeth numbered 1.
	2	Identify the teeth numbered 2.
	3	Identify the teeth numbered 3.
08	1	Identify the region of the tooth numbered 1.
	2	Identify the narrow area of the tooth below the above region numbered 2.
	3	Identify the region of the tooth numbered 3.
	4	Identify the white substance composed of primarily of calcium phosphate and calcium carbonate numbered 4.
	5	Identify the calcified connective tissue (yellowish in color) numbered 5.
09	1	Identify the white substance numbered 1.
	2	Identify the yellowish substance numbered 2.
	3	Identify the connective tissue numbered 3.
	4	Identify the cavity numbered 4.
10	1	Identify the region of the tooth numbered 1.
	2	Identify the region of the tooth numbered 2.
	3	Identify the narrow area between region 1 and 2 numbered 3.
	4	Identify the white substance numbered 4.
	5	Identify the substance numbered 5.
	6	Classify the tooth marked "A".
	7	Classify the tooth marked "B".
11	1	Identify the organ numbered 1.
	2	Identify the organ numbered 2.
12	1	Identify the organ numbered 1.
	2	Identify the duct numbered 2.
	3	Identify the duct numbered 3.

	4	Identify the specific organ numbered 4.
	5	Identify the gland numbered 5.
	6	Identify the organ numbered 6.
	7	Identify the organ (green) numbered 7.
	8	Identify the organ (brown) numbered 8.
13	1	Identify the duct numbered 1.
	2	Identify the sphincter numbered 2.
	3	Identify the duct (white) numbered 3.
	4	Identify the duct (green) numbered 4.
14	1	Identify the organ numbered 1.
	2	Identify the organ numbered 2.
	3	Identify the ducts (green) numbered 3.
	4	Identify the duct (green) numbered 4.
	5	Identify the duct (green) numbered 5.
	6	Identify the duct (yellow-green) numbered 6.
15	1	On the small intestine model, identify the specific layer numbered 1.
	2	On the small intestine model, identify the specific layer numbered 2.
	3	On the small intestine model, identify the specific layer numbered 3.
	4	On the small intestine model, identify the specific layer numbered 4.
	5	On the small intestine model, identify the structure numbered 5.
	6	On the small intestine model, identify the specific vessel numbered 6.
	7	On the small intestine model, identify the specific layer numbered 7.
	8	On the small intestine model, identify the specific tissue numbered 8
16	1	Identify the specific part of the organ numbered 1.
	2	Identify the specific part of the organ numbered 2.
	3	Identify the specific ligament located between structures 1 and 2 numbered 3.
	4	Identify the longitudinal band numbered 4.
	5	Identify the specific serous membrane fold numbered 5.
	6	Identify the specific organ numbered 6.
	7	Identify the organ numbered 7.
	8	Identify the whitish organ numbered 8.
17	1	Identify the specific area numbered 1
	2	Identify the specific area numbered 2.
	3	Identify the specific area numbered 3.
	4	Identify the specific area numbered 4.
	5	Identify the curve numbered 5.
	6	Identify the curve numbered 6.

	7	Identify the specific smooth arrangement marked "A".
	8	Identify the specific smooth arrangement marked "B".
	9	Identify the specific smooth arrangement marked "C".
18	1	Identify the organ numbered 1.
	2	Identify the specific area numbered 2.
	3	Identify the specific area numbered 3.
	4	Identify the bumps numbered 4.
	5	Identify the area numbered 5.
	6	Identify the specific sphincter numbered 6.
	7	Identify the organ numbered 7.
19	1	Identify the organ numbered 1.
	2	Identify the area numbered 2.
	3	Identify the area numbered 3.
	4	Identify the curve numbered 4.
	5	Identify the area numbered 5.
	6	Identify the specific organ numbered 6.
	7	Identify the organ numbered 7.
	8	Identify the organ numbered 8.
20	1	Identify the specific part of the organ numbered 1.
	2	Identify the specific part of the organ numbered 2.
	3	Identify the ligament numbered 3.
21	1	Identify the lobe lettered "A".
	2	Identify the lobe lettered "B".
	3	Identify the lobe lettered "C".
	4	Identify the lobe lettered "D".
	5	Identify the blood vessel numbered 5.
	6	Identify the ligament numbered 6.
	7	Identify the organ numbered 7.
	8	Identify the duct numbered 8.
	9	Identify the ducts numbered 9.
	10	Identify the duct numbered 10.
22	1	Identify the organ numbered 1.
	2	Identify the portion (area) numbered 2.
	3	Identify the portion (area) numbered 3.
	4	Identify the portion (area) numbered 4.
	5	Identify the specific serous membrane fold numbered 5.

	6	Identify the specific serous membrane fold numbered 6.
	7	Identify the specific muscle arrangement lettered "A".
	8	Identify the specific muscle arrangement lettered "B".
	9	Identify the specific muscle arrangement lettered "C".
23	1	Identify the organ numbered 1.
	2	Identify the specific portion (area) numbered 2.
	3	Identify the specific portion (area) numbered 3.
	4	Identify the specific portion (area) numbered 4.
	5	Identify the specific portion (area) numbered 5.
	6	Identify the specific valve numbered 6.
	7	Identify the organ numbered 7l
	8	Identify ridges (bumps) on the mucosa numbered 8.
24	1	Identify the structure numbered 1.
	2	Identify the structure numbered 2.
	3	Identify the structure numbered 3.
	4	Identify the valve numbered 4.
	5	Identify the anatomical portion numbered 5.
	6	Identify the flexure numbered 6.
	7	Identify the anatomical portion numbered 7.
	8	Identify the flexure numbered 8.
	9	Identify the anatomical portion numbered 9.
	10	Identify the anatomical portion numbered 10.
	11	Identify the anatomical portion numbered 11.
	12	Identify the anatomical portion numbered 12.
25	1	Identify the anatomical portion numbered 1.
	2	Identify the structure numbered 2.
	3	Identify the specific sphincter numbered 3.
	4	Identify the specific sphincter numbered 4.
	5	Identify mucous membranes arranged in longitudinal folds numbered 5.
	6	Identify the anatomical portion numbered 6.
26	1	Identify the specific gland numbered 1.
	2	Identify the duct numbered 2.
27	1	Identify the specific part numbered 1.
	2	Identify the specific part numbered 2.
	3	Identify the organ numbered 3.
	4	Identify the longitudinal muscle layer numbered 4.

	5	Identify the pocket like sack (pucker) numbered 5.
	6	Identify the specific anatomical portion numbered 6.
	7	Identify the specific serous membrane fold numbered 7.
28	1	Identify the specific arch in the oral cavity numbered 1.
	2	Identify the specific arch in the oral cavity numbered 2.
	3	Identify the specific structure numbered 3.
	4	Identify the area numbered 4.
29	1	Identify the specific structure numbered 1.
	2	Identify the specific structures numbered 2.
	3	Identify the area numbered 3.
	4	Identify the organ numbered 4.
30	1	Identify the specific structure numbered 1.
	2	Identify the arch in the oral cavity numbered 2.
	3	Identify the arch in the oral cavity numbered 3.
	4	Identify the specific lymphatic tissue numbered 4.
	5	Identify the area in the oral cavity numbered 5.
	6	Identify the specific lymphatic tissue numbered 6.
	7	Identify the structure numbered 7.
31	1	Identify the specific blood vessel on the liver model numbered 1.
	2	Identify the whitish structure on the liver model numbered 2.
	3	Identify the organ (colored green) on the liver model numbered 3.
	4	Identify the lobe on the liver model numbered 4.
	5	Identify the lobe on the liver model numbered 5.
	6	Identify the lobe on the liver model numbered 6.
	7	Identify the lobe on the liver model numbered 7.
	8	Identify the duct (colored green) on the liver model numbered 8
	9	Identify the duct (colored green) on the liver model numbered 9.
	10	Identify the blood vessel (colored red) on the liver model numbered 10.
32	1	Identify the lobe on the liver model numbered 1.
	2	Identify the lobe on the liver model numbered 2.
	3	Identify the lobe on the liver model numbered 3.
	4	Identify the blood vessel on the liver model numbered 4.
	5	Identify the ligament on the superior surface of the live model numbered 5.
33	1	Identify the lobe of the liver model numbered 1.
	2	Identify the lobe of the liver model numbered 2.
	3	Identify the structure (green) on the liver model numbered 3.

	4	Identify the ligament on the liver model numbered 4.

DIGESTIVE SYSTEM
HISTOLOGY
Type **DIGESTIVEHIST** in white space in tool bar to bring up these image

Picture #	Question #	Questions
01	1	Identify the specific epithelial tissue (give cell and arrangement) numbered 1.
	2	Identify the specific structure numbered 2.
02	1	Identify the organ lettered "A".
	2	Identify the structure numbered 2.
03	1	Identify the structure numbered 1.
	2	Structure number 1 is located in which specific layer of the digestive tract?
	3	Identify the specific layer numbered 3.
	4	Identify the specific layer numbered 4.
	5	What is the primary tissue-forming layer numbered 4.
	6	The tissue forming layer number 4 is arranged in how many layers in this organ?
04	1	Identify the specific part of the small intestine numbered "1A".
	2	Identify the specific part of the small intestine numbered "2B".
	3	Identify the specific part of the small intestine numbered "3C".
	4	Identify the specific layer numbered 4.
	5	Identify the specific layer numbered 5.
	6	Identify the specific structures numbered 6. This structure will help you identify what "2B" is.
05	1	Identify the specific organ numbered "5A".
	2	Identify the specific structures numbered 2.
06	1	Identify the specific organ numbered "6A"
	2	Identify the specific unit outline in black, numbered 2.
	3	Identify the white structure numbered 3.
07	1	Identify this specific part of the digestive system.
	2	Identify the specific layer numbered 2.
	3	Identify the glands numbered 3.
	4	Identify the specific layer numbered 4.
	5	Identify the glands numbered 5.
08	1	Identify the organ lettered "8A".
09	1	Identify the organ lettered "9A".
10	1	Identify the organ lettered "10A".

Picture #	Question #	Questions
11	1	Identify the structure numbered 1.

URINARY SYSTEM
MODELS
Type **URINARYMODEL** in white space in tool bar to bring up these image

Picture #	Question #	Questions
01	1	Identify the organ numbered 1.
	2	Identify the gland numbered 2.
	3	Identify the brown fibrous layer numbered 3.
	4	Identify the dilated structure numbered 4.
	5	Identify the structure numbered 5.
	6	Identify the organ numbered 6.
	7	Identify the blood vessel numbered 7.
	8	Identify the blood vessel numbered 8.
	9	Identify the blood vessel numbered 9.
02	1	Identify the structure numbered 1.
	2	Identify the structure numbered 2.
	3	Identify the structure numbered 3.
	4	Identify the structure numbered 4.
	5	Identify the triangle structure numbered 5.
03	1	Identify the brown layer numbered 1.
	2	Identify the concave area on the medial surface numbered 2.
04	1	Identify the structure numbered 1.
	2	Identify the structure numbered 2.
	3	Identify the structure numbered 3.
	4	Identify the apex end ("nipple" structure) of the triangle structure numbered 4.
	5	Identify the triangle structure (green arrows) numbered 5.
05	1	Identify the organ numbered 1.
	2	Identify the structure numbered 2.
	3	Identify the organ numbered 3.
	4	Identify the space numbered 4.
	5	Identify the structure numbered 5.
	6	Identify the structure numbered 6.
06	1	Identify the blood vessel numbered 1.
	2	Identify the blood vessel numbered 2.
	3	Identify the blood vessel numbered 3.

	4	Identify the blood vessel numbered 4.
	5	Identify the blood vessel numbered 5.
	6	Identify the blood vessel numbered 6.
07	1	Identify the tubular structure numbered 1.
	2	Identify the space numbered 2.
	3	Identify the structure numbered 3.
	4	Identify the structure numbered 4.
	5	Identify the structure numbered 5.
	6	Identify the structure numbered 6.
	6	Identify the area numbered 7.
08	1	Identify the area numbered 1.
	2	Identify the structure numbered 2.
09	1	Identify the structure numbered 1.
	2	Identify the space numbered 2.
	3	Identify the structure numbered 3.
	4	Identify the structure numbered 4.
	5	Identify the "nipple" like structure numbered 5.
	6	Identify the area numbered 6.
	7	Identify the blood vessel numbered 7.
	8	Identify the blood vessel numbered 8.
	9	Identify the blood vessel numbered 9.
10	1	Identify the structure numbered 1.
	2	Identify the structure numbered 2.
	3	Identify the structure numbered 3.
	4	Identify the region numbered 4.
	5	Identify the structure (red lines) numbered 5.
11	1	Identify the structure numbered 1.
	2	Identify the structure numbered 2.
	3	Identify the structure numbered 3.
	4	Identify the region of the kidney numbered 4.
12	1	Identify the structure numbered 1.
	2	Identify the external layer of the structure numbered 2. This simple squamous epithelium layer plays no part in forming filtrate.
	3	Identify the area numbered 3.
	4	Identify the blood vessel numbered 4.
	5	Identify the blood vessel numbered 5.
	6	Identify the blood vessel numbered 6.

	7	Identify the group of cells numbered 7.
13	1	Identify the structure (gray layer) numbered 1.
	2	Identify the cell (white) numbered 2.
	3	Identify the footlike white structure numbered 3.
14	1	Identify the structure numbered 1.
	2	Identify the structure numbered 2.
	3	Identify the structure numbered 3
	4	Identify the structure numbered 4.
	5	Identify the structure numbered 5.
	6	Identify the structure numbered 6.
	7	Identify the blood vessel numbered 7.
	8	Identify the blood vessel numbered 8.
15	1	Identify the type of nephron lettered "A".
	2	Identify the type of nephron lettered "B"
16	1	Identify the blood vessel numbered 1.
	2	Identify the specific structure numbered 2.
	3	Identify the cup shaped structure numbered 3.
	4	Identify the cell numbered 4.
	5	Identify the blood vessel numbered 5.
	6	Identify the structure numbered 6.
	7	Identify the structure numbered 7.
17	1	Identify the blood vessel numbered 1.
	2	Identify the blood vessel numbered 2.
	3	Identify the group of cells numbered 3.
	4	Identify the group of blood vessels numbered 4.
	5	Identify the space numbered 5.
	6	Identify the layer numbered 6.
	7	Identify the structure numbered 7.
18	1	Identify the structure numbered 1.
	2	Identify the structure numbered 2.
	3	Identify the structure numbered 3.
	4	Identify the structure numbered 4.
	5	Identify the structure numbered 5.
	6	Identify the structure numbered 6.
19	1	Identify the specific area numbered 1.
	2	Identify the triangle shaped structure numbered 2.
	3	Identify the area in the kidney numbered 3.

Picture #	Question #	Questions
	4	Identify the red lines numbered 4.
	5	Identify the nipple shaped structure numbered 5.
	6	Identify the structure numbered 6.
20	1	Identify the openings numbered 1.
	2	Identify the area (colored light blue) numbered 2.
	3	Identify the opening numbered 3.
	4	Identify the smooth muscle numbered 4.
	5	Identify the gland numbered 5.
	6	Identify the tube structure numbered 6.
	7	Identify the smooth muscle structure numbered 7.
21	1	Identify the structure numbered 1.
	2	Identify the gland numbered 2.
	3	Identify the gland numbered 3.
22	1	Identify the specific part of the nephron numbered 1.
	2	Identify the specific group of blood capillaries of the nephron numbered 2.
	3	The region of the kidney numbered 3.
	4	Identify the specific blood vessel numbered 4.
	5	Identify the specific blood vessel numbered 5.
	6	Identify the specific tubular structure numbered 6.
	7	Identify the specific tubular structure numbered 7.
	8	Identify the specific tubular structure numbered 8.
	9	Identify the specific tubular structure numbered 9.
	10	Identify the specific tubular structure numbered 10.
	11	Identify the specific tubular structure numbered 11.
	12	Identify the specific group of blood vessels numbered 12.
	13	Identify the specific artery numbered 13.
	14	Identify the specific artery numbered 14.
	15	Identify the specific vein numbered 15.
	16	Identify the specific vein numbered 16.
	17	Identify the specific vein numbered 17.
	18	Identify the specific group of blood vessels numbered 18 located in the medulla region of the kidney.

URINARY SYSTEM
DISSECTIONS
Type **URINARYDISS** white space in tool bar to bring up these image

Picture #	Question #	Questions

01	1	Identify the anatomical area in the kidney numbered 1.
	2	Identify the structure numbered 2.
	3	Identify the structure (passageway) numbered 3.
	4	Identify the structure (passageway) numbered 4.
02	1	Identify the layer numbered 1.
	2	Identify the anatomical area numbered 2.
	3	Identify the structure numbered 3.
	4	Identify the passageway numbered 4.
	5	Identify the passageway numbered 5.
	6	Identify the concave area numbered 6.
	7	Identify the structure numbered 7.

URINARY SYSTEM
HISTOLOG
Type **URINARYHIST** in white space in tool bar to bring up these image

Picture #	Question #	Questions
01	1	Identify the organ lettered "1A".
	2	Identify the entire structure numbered 2 (white and reddish area)
02	1	Identify the specific structure numbered 1 (white area).
	2	Identify the specific structure numbered 2.
03	1	Identify the organ lettered "3A'.
	2	Identify the specific structure numbered 2.
04	1	Identify the specific tubular structure numbered 1.
	2	Identify the specific structure numbered 2.
	3	Identify the white space numbered 3.
05	1	Identify the organ lettered "5A".
	2	Identify the entire structure (white and blue-red) numbered 2.

THE REPRODUCTIVE SYSTEM (MALE)
MODELS
Type **MALEREPRODMODEL** white space in tool bar to bring up these image

Picture #	Question #	Questions
01	1	Identify the specific part numbered 1.
	2	Identify the structure numbered 2.
	3	Identify the gland numbered 3.
	4	Identify the structure numbered 4.

	5	Identify the structure numbered 5.
	6	Identify the organ numbered 6.
	7	Identify the tubular structure numbered 7.
	8.	Identify the tubular structure numbered 8.
	9	Identify the structure numbered 9.
	10	Identify the gland numbered 10.
	11	Identify the gland numbered 11.
02	1	Identify the organ numbered 1.
	2	Identify the tubular structure numbered 2.
	3	Identify the gland numbered 3.
	4	Identify the tubular structure numbered 4.
	5	Identify the gland numbered 5.
03	1	Identify the organ numbered 1.
	2	Identify the gland numbered 2.
	3	Identify the gland numbered 3.
	4	Identify the structure numbered 4.
	5	Identify the gland numbered 5.
04	1	Identify the organ numbered 1.
	2	Identify the structure numbered 2.
	3	Identify the structure numbered 3.
	4	Identify the gland numbered 4.
	5	Identify the gland numbered 5.
05	1	Identify the structure numbered 1.
	2	Identify the specific tubular structure numbered 2.
	3	Identify the erectile tissue numbered 3.
	4	Identify the erectile tissue numbered 4.
	5	Identify the specific tubular structure numbered 5.
	6	Identify the tubular structure numbered 6.
	7	Identify the gland numbered 7.
	8	Identify the erectile tissue numbered 8.
06	1	Identify the structure numbered 1.
	2	Identify the gland numbered 2.
	3	Identify the specific tubular structure numbered 3.
	4	Identify the specific tubular structure numbered 4.
	5	Identify the specific tubular structure numbered 5.
	6	Identify the specific tubular structure numbered 6.
07	1	Identify the erectile tissue numbered 1.

	2	Identify the tubular structure numbered 2.
	3	Identify the erectile tissue numbered 3.
	4	Identify the structure numbered 4.
	5	Identify the structure numbered 5.
	6	Identify the structure numbered 6.
	7	Identify the structure numbered 7.
	8	Identify the tubular structure numbered 8.
08	1	Identify the erectile tissue numbered 1.
	2	Identify the erectile tissue numbered 2.
	3	Identify the opening numbered 3.
09	1	Identify the organ numbered 1.
	2	Identify the structure numbered 2.
	3	Identify the gland numbered 3.
	4	Identify the gland numbered 4.
10	1	Identify the opening in the abdominal wall numbered 1.
	2	Identify the specific skeletal muscle numbered 2.
	3	Identify the specific smooth muscle numbered 3.
	4	Identify the specific serous membrane numbered 4.
	5	Identify the specific serous membrane numbered 5.
11	1	Identify the structure numbered 1.
	2	Identify the part numbered 2.
	3	Identify the part numbered 3.
	4	Identify the accessory gland numbered 4.
	5	Identify the accessory gland numbered 5.
	6	Identify the accessory gland numbered 6.
	7	Identify the organ numbered 7.
	8	Identify the structure numbered 8.
	9	Identify the structure numbered 9.

THE REPRODUCTIVE SYSTEM (MALE)
DISSECTIONS
Type **MALEDISSECT** space in tool bar to bring up these image

Picture #	Question #	Questions
01	1	Identify the organ on the dissection numbered 1.
	2	Identify the structure on the dissection numbered 2.
02	1	Identify the organ and serous membrane on the dissection numbered 1.

	2	Identify the specific part of the structure on the dissection numbered 2.
	3	Identify the specific serous membrane on the dissection numbered 3.
	4	Identify the tubular structure on the dissection numbered 4.
03	1	Identify the organ on the dissection numbered 1.
	2	Identify the specific part of the structure on the dissection numbered 2.
	3	Identify the structure on the dissection numbered 3.
	4	Identify the structure on the dissection numbered 4.
	5	Identify the specific part of the structure on the dissection numbered 5.
	6	Identify the specific part of the structure on the dissection numbered 6.

THE REPRODUCTIVE SYSTEM (MALE)
HISTOLOGY
Type **MALEREPDHIST** white space in tool bar to bring up these image

Picture #	Question #	Questions
01	1	Identify the organ lettered "A".
	2	Identify the space numbered 2.
	3	Identify the erectile tissue numbered 3.
	4	Identify the space numbered 4
02	1	Identify the structure numbered 1.
	2	Identify the structure numbered 2.
	3.	Identify the entire structure (light yellow) numbered 3.
	4.	Identify the structure numbered 4.
03	1	Identify the specific part numbered 1 of this cell.
	2	What material is contained within the structure numbered 2.
	3	Identify the specific part numbered 3.
04	1	Identify the specific cell structure numbered 1.
	2	What is the function of structure numbered 1.
05	1	Identify the organ this organ.
06	1	Identify the cells numbered 1.
07	1	Identify the specific structure numbered 1.
	2	What is the function of structure numbered 1.
	3	Identify the cells numbered 3.

THE REPRODUCTIVE SYSTEM (FEMALE)
MODELS
Type **FEMALEREPRODMODEL** white space in tool bar to bring up these image

Picture #	Question #	Questions
01	1	Identify the specific part of the vulva numbered 1.
	2	Identify the specific part of the vulva numbered 2.
	3	Identify the specific part of the vulva numbered 3.
	4	Identify the organ numbered 4.
	5	Identify the tubular structure numbered 5.
	6	Identify the organ numbered 6.
	7	Identify the structure numbered 7.
	8	Identify the structure numbered 8.
	9	Identify the structure numbered 9.
	10	Identify the organ numbered 10.
	11	Identify the structure numbered 11.
02	1	Identify the organ numbered 1.
	2	Identify the specific numbered 2.
	3	Identify the specific numbered 3.
	4	Identify the specific numbered 4.
	5	Identify fingerlike projections numbered 5.
	6	Identify the organ numbered 6.
	7	Identify the specific part of the vulva numbered 7.
	8	Identify the specific part of the vulva numbered 8.
03	1	Identify the specific part of the vulva numbered 1.
	2	Identify the specific bone structure numbered 2.
	3	Identify the specific erectile tissue numbered 3.
	4	Identify the specific part of the vulva numbered 4.
	5	Identify the specific part of the vulva numbered 5.
	6	Identify the structure numbered 6.
	7	Identify the structure numbered 7.
	8	Identify the specific portion and organ numbered 8.
	9	Identify the specific portion and organ numbered 9.
	10	Identify the specific portion and organ numbered 10.
	11	Identify the structure numbered 11.
04	1	Identify the structure numbered 1.
	2	Identify the structure numbered 2.
	3	Identify the area numbered 3.
	4	Identify the opening numbered 4.
	5	Identify the opening numbered 5.
05	1	Identify the ligament numbered 1.

	2	Identify the structure numbered 2.
	3	Identify the gland numbered 3.
	4	Identify the finger like projections numbered 4.
	5	Identify the funnel-shaped structure numbered 5.
	6	Identify the specific part and organ numbered 6.
	7	Identify the part of the vulva numbered 7.
06	1	Identify the specific part numbered 1.
	2	Identify the specific part numbered 2.
	3	Identify the specific part numbered 3.
	4	Identify the ligament numbered 4.
	5	Identify the structure numbered 5.
	6	Identify the structure numbered 6.
07	1	Identify the indentations numbered 1.
	2	Identify the indentation numbered 2.
	3	Identify the structure numbered 3.
	4	Identify the cavity numbered 4.
	5	Identify the cavity numbered 5.
	6	Identify the organ numbered 6.
	7	Identify the indentation numbered 7.
08	1	Identify the organ numbered 1.
	2	Identify the organ numbered 2.
	3	Identify the structure numbered 3.
	4	Identify the structure numbered 4.
09	1	Identify the specific part of the broad ligament numbered 1.
	2	Identify the specific part of the broad ligament numbered 2.
	3	Identify the specific part of the broad ligament numbered 3.
10	1	Identify the structure numbered 1.
	2	Identify the ligament numbered 2.
	3	Identify the ligament numbered 3.
11	1	Identify the specific part numbered 1.
	2	Identify the cavity numbered 2.
	3	Identify the cavity numbered 3.
	4	Identify the ligament numbered 4.
	5	Identify the ligament numbered 5.
	6	Identify the specific part of the uterine tube numbered 6.
	7	Identify the specific part numbered 7.
	8	Identify the ridges numbered 8.

	9	Identify the narrow area numbered 9.
12	1	Identify the specific layer numbered 1.
	2	Identify the specific layer numbered 2.
	3	Identify the specific layer numbered 3.
13	1	Identify the specific ligament numbered 1.
	2	Identify the specific layer numbered 2.
	3	Identify the inner part of the layer (white) 3.
	4	Identify the indentation numbered 4.
14	1	Identify the ligament numbered 1.
	2	Identify the ligament numbered 2.
	3	Identify the ligament numbered 3.
	4	Identify the ligament numbered 4.
15	1	Identify the structure numbered 1.
	2	Identify the structure numbered 2
	3	Identify the ligament numbered 3.
	4	Identify the specific region of the uterus numbered 4.
	5	Identify the structure numbered 5.
	6	Identify the structure numbered 6.
16	1	Identify the specific region of the uterus numbered 1.
	2	Identify the structure numbered 2.
	3	Identify the structure numbered 3.
	4	Identify the structure numbered 4.
	5	Identify the structure numbered 5.
17	1	Identify the structure numbered 1.
	2	Identify the structure numbered 2.
	3	Identify the structure numbered 3.
	4	Identify the gland numbered 4.
	5	Identify the sphincter numbered 5.
	6	Identify the opening numbered 6.
18	1	Identify the ligament numbered 1.
	2	Identify the structure numbered 2.
	3	Identify the ligament numbered 3.
	4	Identify the structure numbered 4.
	5	Identify the ligament numbered 5.
	6	Identify the ligament numbered 6.
	7	Identify the specific region of the uterus numbered 7.

	8	Identify the specific region of the uterus numbered 8.
19	1	Identify the specific connective tissue numbered 1.
	2	Identify the vessels numbered 2.
	3	Identify the structure numbered 3.
	4	Identify the structure numbered 4.
	5	Identify the duct numbered 5.
	6	Identify the gland numbered 6.
20	1	Identify the structure numbered 1.
	2	Identify the region numbered 2.
	3	Identify the structure numbered 3.
	4	Identify the folds numbered 4.
	5	Identify the structure numbered 5.
	6	Identify the structure numbered 6.
	7	Identify the ligament numbered 7.
	8	Identify the specific region of the uterus numbered 8.

THE REPRODUCTIVE SYSTEM (FEMALE)
HISTOLOGY
Type **femalehist** white space in tool bar to bring up these image

Picture #	Question #	Questions
01	1	Identify the organ lettered "A".
	2	Identify the specific cell structure numbered 2.
	3	Identify the specific cell structure numbered 3.
	4.	Identify the entire cell structure numbered 4.
	5	Identify the clear area numbered 5.
	6	Identify the specific cell numbered 6.
02	1	Identify the cells numbered 1.
03	1	Identify the cell structure lettered "B".
	2	Identify the space numbered 2.
	3	Identify the specific cell numbered 3.
	4	Identify the clear glycoprotein layer numbered 4.
	5	Identify the group of cells numbered 5.
04	1	Identify the cells numbered 1.
05	1	Identify the specific structure (outlined in black) numbered 1.
06	1	Identify the organ lettered "C".
07	1	Identify the specific gland numbered 1.
08	1	Identify the specific gland numbered 1.
09	1	Identify the cells numbered 1.
	2	Identify the cell structure numbered 2.

10	1	Identify the endocrine gland numbered 1.
11	1	Identify the structure numbered 1.

ANSWERS
Human Anatomy
& Physiology II

Picture #	Question #	answers
01	1	Thyroid gland
02	1	Pancreas
	2	Adrenal glands
03	1	Pancreas
	2	Adrenal glands
04	1	Primordial follicles
	2	Primary (preantral) follicles
	3	Secondary follicle
	4	Follicular fluid in antrum Graafian (vesicular or mature) follicle
	5	Corpus luteum
	6	Corpus albicans
	7	Secondary oocyte (ovulated oocyte surrounded by corona radiata)
	8	Germinal epithelium
05	1	Thyroid gland
	2	Isthmus of thyroid gland
06	1	Parathyroid glands
	2	Thyroid gland

ENDOCRINE HISTOLOGY
ANSWERS

Picture #	Question #	answers
01	1	Pancreas
	2	Islet of Langerhan or pancreatic islet
	3.	Acinar cells
	4.	Acini cells produce digestive enzymes
02	1	Pituitary gland
	2	Anterior (adenohypophysis) or anterior lobe
	3	Growth hormone (GH) Prolactin (LTH) Thyroid stimulating hormone (TSH) Adrenocorticotropic hormone (ACTH) Follicle-stimulating hormone (FSH) Luteinizing hormone (LH) Melanocyte-stimulating hormone (MSH)
	4	Posterior (neurohypophysis) gland or posterior lobe

	5	None (only stores oxytocin and ADH)
03	1	Posterior pituitary (neurohypophysis)
	2	Anterior pituitary (adenohypophysis)
04	1.	Adrenal gland
	2	Zona glomerulosa
	3	Zona fasciculata
	4	Zona reticularis
	5	Adrenal medulla
	6	Sinusoids
05	1	Pancreas
	2	Islet of Langerhan
	3	Alpha (glucagon) Beta (insulin) Delta (somatostatin) F-cells (polypeptides that are released into the blood after a meal that regulates production of pancreatic enzymes)
06	1.	Thyroid gland
	2	Parathyroid gland
07	1	Follicle of thyroid gland
	2	Colloid
	3	Parafollicular or c- cells
08	1	Thymus gland
	2	Hassall's (thymic) corpuscle
09	1	Ovary
	2	Primordial follicle
	3	Primary follicle
	4	Graafian or mature follicle
	5	Zona pellucida
	6	Secondary oocyte
10		No image to answer
11	1	Seminiferous tubules of testis
	2	Interstitial or Leydig cells of testis
12	1	Corpus luteum
13	1	Anterior pituitary (adenohypophysis)
14	1	Thyroid gland
15	1	Anterior pituitary (adenohypophysis)
16	1	Thyroid gland
	2	Parathyroid gland
17	1	Posterior (neurohypophysis) gland or posterior lobe
	2	Pituicytes
18	1	Follicular cells of thyroid gland

	2	Thyroglobulin
19	1	Parathyroid gland
20	1	Pancreas
	2	Islet of Langerhans (pancreatic islet)
21	1	Islet of Langerhans (pancreatic islet) of pancreas
22	1	Adrenal medulla
	2	Zona reticularis
	3	Zona fasciculata
	4	Zona glomerulosa
	5	Capsule
23	1	Adrenal medulla
	2	Adrenal cortex
24	1	Pancreas
	2	Islet of Langerhan (pancreatic islet)
	3	Acinar cells
	4	Acini cells produce digestive enzymes for the exocrine part of the pancreas

THE CARDIOVASCULAR SYSTEM: BLOOD
BLOOD CELLS MODELS
ANSWERS

Picture #	Question #	answers
01	1	Monocyte leukocyte (WBC)
	2	Nucleus
02	1	neutrophil leukocyte (WBC)
	2	Lobed nucleus
	3	Granules
03	1	Erythrocyte (red blood cell, RBC)
	2	Area in red blood cell where nucleus was. Remember that the adult human erythrocyte is enucleated.
04	1	eosinophil leukocyte (WBC)
	2	Lobed nucleus
	3	Cytoplasmic granules
05	1	Lymphocyte leukocyte (WBC)
	2	Spherical or indented nucleus
06	1	Basophil leukocyte (WBC)
07	1	Erythrocyte (red blood cell, RBC)
	2	Eosinophil leukocyte (WBC). Note: bilobed nucleus and red cytoplasmic granules
	3	Red blood cell
	4	Leukocyte (WBC)
08	1	Red blood cells (erythrocytes)

BLOOD CELLS
HISTOLOGY
ANSWERS

Picture #	Question #	answers
01	1	Natural Killer Cell
	2	Nucleus
	3	Erythrocyte (rbc)
02	1	Eosinophil
	2	Granules
03	1	Basophil
04	1	Neutrophil
	2	Lobed nuclei
05	1	Monocyte
06	1	Platelets
	2	Lymphocyte
07	1	Neutrophil
	2	Erythrocytes
08	1	Neutrophil
09	1	Monocyte
	2	Neutrophil
	3	Lymphocyte
	4	Erythrocyte
	5	Platelets
10	1	Erythrocyte (notice the biconcave disc appearance)
11	1	Basophil
12	1	Lymphocyte
13	1	Reticulocyte
		General Knowledge Information
	14	Lymphocyte and monocyte
	15	Eosinophil, basophil and neutrophil`
	16	Eosinophil, basophil, neutrophil
	17	Lymphocyte, monocyte

Picture #	Question #	answers
01	1	Thoracic cavity
02	1	Mediastinum within thoracic cavity
03	1	Right atrium
	2	Apex formed by left ventricle
	3	Right ventricle
	4	Left auricle
	5	Superior vena cava
	6	Ascending aorta
04	1	Right auricle
	2	Left auricle
	3	Myocardium of right ventricle
	4	Apex formed by left myocardium of ventricle
	5	Superior vena cava
	6	Inferior vena cava
	7	Pulmonary trunk (artery)
	8	Ascending aorta
	9	Brachiocephalic artery
	10	Left common carotid artery
	11	Left subclavian artery
	12	Left pulmonary artery
	13	Ligamentum arteriosum
	14	Left pulmonary veins
05	1	Right auricle
	2	Left auricle
	3	Right ventricle
	4	Left ventricle
	5	Apex
	6	Ascending aorta
	7	Superior vena cava
	8	Pulmonary trunk (artery)
	9	Left pulmonary artery
	10	Left pulmonary vein
06	1	Right auricle
	2	Left auricle

	3	Ascending aorta
	4	Superior vena cava
	5	Pulmonary trunk (artery)
	6	Left pulmonary artery
	7	Right ventricle
	8 (Yellow)	Left ventricle
	8 (Black)	Apex of heart
	9	Ligamentum arteriosum
07	1	Ascending aorta
	2	Pulmonary trunk (artery)
	3	Superior vena cava
	4	Inferior vena cava
	5	Right pulmonary veins
	6	Right auricle
	7	Left auricle
	8	Right coronary artery (in right atrioventricular groove)
	9	Left coronary artery (in left atrioventricular groove)
	10	Apex
	11	Left brachiocephalic vein
	12	Right brachiocephalic vein
08	1	Left coronary artery
	2	Anterior interventricular artery of left coronary artery
	3	Right coronary artery
	4	Marginal branch of right coronary artery
	5	Posterior interventricular artery of right coronary artery
	6	Great cardiac vein
	7	Circumflex artery of left coronary artery
	8	Right auricle
	9	Pulmonary trunk (artery)
	10	Ascending aorta
	11	Superior vena cava
09	1	Left pulmonary veins
	2	Descending aorta (thoracic aorta)
	3	Left pulmonary artery
	4	Left subclavian artery
	5	Myocardium of left ventricle
10	1	Left coronary artery

	2	Right coronary artery
	3	Anterior interventricular artery (in anterior interventricular sulcus)
	4	Circumflex artery
	5	Continuation of right coronary artery
	6	Marginal artery of right coronary artery
	7	Posterior interventricular branch of right coronary artery
	8	Great cardiac vein
11	1	Left atrium
	2	Right pulmonary veins
	3	Left pulmonary veins
	4	Inferior vena cava
12	1	Coronary sinus
	2	Inferior vena cava
	3	Left pulmonary veins
	4	Right pulmonary veins
	5	Middle cardiac vein
	6	Posterior interventricular artery
13	1	Right auricle
	2	Left atrium
	3.	Left pulmonary veins
	4	Pulmonary trunk (artery)
	5	Ascending aorta
	6	Brachiocephalic artery
	7	Left common carotid artery
	8	Left subclavian artery
	9	Right ventricle
	10	Papillary muscle
	11	Ligamentum arteriosum
14	1	Right atrium
	2	Fossa ovalis
	3	Pectinate muscles
	4	Inferior vena cava
	5	Trabeculae carneae
15	1	Right atrium
	2	Tricuspid valve
	3	Pulmonary semilunar valve

	4	Right ventricle
	5	Pulmonary trunk (artery)
16	1	Left atrium
	2	Left pulmonary veins
	3	Right pulmonary veins
	4	Bicuspid (mitral) valve cuspid
	5	Chordae tendineae of bicuspid valve
	6	Papillary muscle
	7	Trabeculae carneae
	8	Pulmonary trunk (artery)
	9	Left pulmonary artery
	10	Ligamentum arteriosum
	11	Left subclavian artery
	12	Left common carotid artery
	13	Brachiocephalic artery
	14	Pectinate muscles
17	1	Aortic semilunar valve
	2	Right and left pulmonary veins
	3	Left ventricle
18	1	Right atrium
	2	Superior vena cava
	3	Pectinate muscles
	4	Tricuspid valve
	5	Chordae tendineae
	6	Interventricular septum
	7	Left atrium
	8	Bicuspid (mitral) valve
	9	Chordae tendineae
	10	Papillary muscle
	11	Apex
	12	Pulmonary semilunar valve
19	1	Sinoatrial (SA) node "pacemaker"
	2	Fossa ovalis
	3	Atrioventricular (AV) node
	4	Left auricle
	5	Left atrium
	6	Left pulmonary veins

	7	Left and right coronary arteries
	8	Cusps of tricuspid valve
	9	Chordae tendineae
	10	Papillary muscles
20	1	Left coronary artery
	2	Circumflex branch (artery)
	3	Anterior interventricular branch (artery)
	4	Right coronary artery
	5	Posterior interventricular branch (artery)
	6	Marginal branch (artery)
	7	Great cardiac vein
21	1	Pulmonary semilunar valve
	2	Bicuspid (mitral) valve
	3	Tricuspid valve
	4	Chordae tendinae
	5	Papillary muscle

SHEEP HEART
DISSECTIONS
ANSWERS

Picture #	Question #	answers
01	1	Auricle of right atrium
	2	Auricle of left atrium
	3	Right ventricle
	4	Left ventricle
	5	Apex of heart (left ventricle)
	6	Pulmonary trunk (artery)
	7	Ascending aorta
02	1	Auricle of right atrium
	2	Auricle of left atrium
	3	Ascending aorta
	4	Right ventricle
	5	Left ventricle
	6	Anterior interventricular sulcus
03	1	Superior vena cava
	2	Pulmonary trunk (artery)

	3	Ascending aorta
	4	Myocardium of right ventricle
	5	Myocardium of left ventricle
04	1	Auricle of left atrium
	2	Pulmonary trunk (artery)
05	1	Cuspids of bicuspid (mitral) valve. Notice thickness of myocardium of left ventricle
	2	Chordae tendinae
06	1	Epicardium (visceral layer of serous pericardium)
	2	Myocardium of left ventricle
	3	Endocardium
07	1	Epicardium (visceral layer of serous pericardium)
	2	Myocardium composed of cardiac muscle
	3	Endocardium
	4	Left ventricle (notice thickness of myocardium)
	5	Right ventricle (compare thickness of right ventricle myocardium to left ventricle myocardium)
08	1	Pulmonary trunk (artery)
	2	Aorta
	3	Superior vena cava
	4	Auricle of left atrium
09	1	Four (4) pulmonary veins
	2	Aorta
	3	Auricle of left atrium
10	1	Right ventricle
	2	Papillary muscles
	3	Chordae tendineae
	4	Cusp of bicuspid (mitral) valve
	5	Left atrium
	6	Myocardium of left ventricle
11	1	Cusp of tricuspid valve
	2	Right atrium
	3	Right ventricle
	4	Aorta
	5	Superior vena cava
	6	Pulmonary trunk (artery)
	7	Ligamentum arteriosum

	8	Left atrium
	9	Cusp of bicuspid (mitral) valve
	10	Chordae tendineae
	11	Left ventricle
	12	Papillary muscles of left ventricle
	13	Pulmonary semilunar valve

THE CARDIOVASCULAR SYSTEM: BLOOD VESSELS (MODELS)
ANSWERS

Picture #	Question #	answers
01	1	auricle of right atrium
	2	Superior vena cava
	3	Left and right Brachiocephalic veins
	4	Right internal jugular vein
	5	Right subclavian vein
	6	Left internal jugular vein
	7	Left external jugular vein
	8	Left subclavian vein
	9	Left axillary vein
02	1	Left Internal jugular vein
	2	Left subclavian vein
	3	Right brachiocephalic vein
	4	Superior vena cava
	5	Inferior vena cava
	6	Abdominal aorta
03	1	Right subclavian vein
	2	Right internal jugular vein
	3	Right and left brachiocephalic veins
	4	Superior vena cava
	5	Ascending aorta or arch of aorta
	6	Right common carotid artery
	7	Left common carotid artery
	8	Inferior vena cava
04	1	Left and right vertebral artery (notice transverse foramen)
	2	Right common carotid artery

05	1	Right coronary artery
	2	Marginal branch of right coronary artery
	3	Posterior interventricular branch of right coronary artery
06	1	Inferior vena cava
	2	Renal vein
	3	Abdominal aorta
	4	Superior mesenteric artery
	5	Celiac trunk
	6	Left gonadal (ovarian in female, testicular in male) artery
	7	Inferior mesenteric artery
	8	Right common iliac artery
	9	Left common iliac artery
	10	Left internal iliac artery
	11 (RED)	Right external iliac artery
	11 (BLUE)	Left common iliac vein
07	1	Inferior vena cava
	2	Abdominal aorta
	3	Celiac trunk
	4	Superior mesenteric artery
	5	Right gonadal (testicular) artery
	6	Inferior mesenteric artery
	7	Renal artery
	8	Left common iliac artery
08	1	Left common carotid artery
	2	Right common carotid artery
	3	Right vertebral artery
	4	Right subclavian artery
	5	Left internal carotid artery
	6	Left external carotid artery
	7	Ascending aorta
09	1	Ascending aorta
	2	Right common carotid
	3	Left common carotid
	4	Right subclavian artery
	5	Left subclavian artery
10	1	Superior vena cava
	2	Brachiocephalic veins

	3	Right internal jugular
	4	Left internal jugular
	5	Left external jugular
	6	Left subclavian vein
	7	Pulmonary trunk (artery)
	8	Right external jugular
11	1	Right external jugular
	2	Right internal jugular
	3	Left internal jugular
	4	Left external jugular
	5	Brachiocephalic vein
	6	Superior vena cava
12	1	Right pulmonary veins
	2	Descending aorta or thoracic aorta
	3	Brachiocephalic artery
	4	Right common carotid
	5	Left common carotid
	6	Left subclavian artery
	7	Azygos vein
13	1	Right internal jugular
	2	Right common carotid
	3	Right subclavian artery
	4	Brachiocephalic artery
	5	Left common carotid
	6	Left subclavian artery
	7	Thoracic aorta
	8	Right pulmonary arteries taking blood to right lung
	9	Right pulmonary veins bring blood from right lung to heart
	10	Azygos vein
14	1	Axillary artery
	2	Brachial artery
	3	Ulnar artery
	4	Radial artery
15	1	Superior vena cava
	2	Right brachiocephalic vein
	3	Right internal jugular

	4	Right external jugular
	5	Axillary vein
	6	Basilic vein
	7	Brachial vein
	8	Cephalic vein (showing entire length)
	9	Median cubital vein
	10	Radial vein
	11	Right subclavian vein
	12	Ulnar vein
16	1	Splenic artery
	2	Renal artery
	3	Inferior mesenteric artery
	4	Right common iliac artery
	5	Right internal iliac artery
	6	Right external iliac artery
17	1	Celiac trunk (artery)
	2	Superior mesenteric artery
18	1	Celiac trunk (splenic artery branching off)
	2	Superior mesenteric artery
	3	Right common iliac artery
	4	Right internal iliac artery
	5	Right external iliac artery
	6	Inferior vena cava
	7	Renal vein
19	1	Femoral artery
	2	Anterior tibial artery
	3	Dorsalis pedis artery
	4	Greater saphenous vein
	5	Femoral vein
	6	Popliteal vein
	7	Anterior tibial vein
20	1	Inferior vena cava
	2	Abdominal aorta
	3	Celiac trunk
	4	Superior mesenteric artery
	5	Gonadal arteries
	6	Inferior mesenteric artery

	7	Left common iliac artery
	8	Renal artery
	9	Renal vein
21	1	Median cubital vein
	2	Basilic vein
	3	Cephalic vein
	4	Brachial vein
	5	Axillary vein
	6	Subclavian vein
	7	Right brachiocephalic vein
	8	Superior vena cava
	9	Internal jugular vein
	10	External jugular vein
22	1	Hepatic portal vein
	2	Renal vein
	3	Celiac trunk (artery)
	4	Superior mesenteric artery
	5	Abdominal aorta
23	1	Left common carotid
	2	Right common carotid
	3	Right vertebral artery
	4	Basilar artery
24	1	Left subclavian vein
	2	Left external
	3	Left internal jugular
	4	Left brachiocephalic vein)
	5	Superior vena cava
25	1	Celiac trunk
	2	Superior mesenteric artery
	3	Right common iliac artery
	4	Left gonadal artery
	5	Inferior mesenteric artery
26	1	Thoracic aorta
	2	Aortic arch
	3	Posterior intercostal arteries
	4	Superior vena cava

	5	Inferior vena cava
27	1	Vein
	2	Artery
	3	Endothelium; Tunica interna
	4	Tunica media
	5	Tunica externa
	6	Venous valve
28	1	Endothelium; Tunica interna
	2	Internal elastic lamina
	3	Tunica media
	4	External elastic lamina
	5	Tunica externa
29	1	Skeletal muscle
	2	Varicose vein
30	1	Endothelium; Tunica interna
	2	Tunica media
	3	Tunica externa

THE CARDIOVASCULAR SYSTEM: BLOOD VESSELS
HISTOLOGY
ANSWERS

Picture #	Question #	answers
01	1	Artery
	2	Vein
	3	Tunica media
	4	Tunica interna
02	1	Artery

RESPIRATORY SYSTEM
MODELS
ANSWERS

Picture #	Question #	answers
01	1	Frontal sinus
	2	Middle concha
	3	Middle meatus
	4	External nare (nostrils)

	5	Vestibule
	6	Inferior meatus
	7	Pharyngeal (adenoids) tonsil
	8	Sphenoid sinus
	9	Opening of auditory (Eustachian) or pharyngotympanic tube
	10	Internal nares
	11	Inferior concha
	12	Superior concha
02	1	Apex
	2	Base
	3	Cardiac notch
	4	Parietal pleura
	5	Pleural cavity (normally contains fluid secreted by the membrane to reduce friction between the membranes and allows them to slide easily on one another during breathing)
	6	Visceral pleura
	7	Right
	8	left
03	1	Diaphragm
	2	Superior lobe of right lung
	3	Middle lobe of right lung
	4	Inferior lobe of right lung
	5	Superior lobe of left lung
	6	Inferior lobe of left lung
	7	Horizontal fissure
	8	Oblique fissure
	9	Oblique fissure
	9*	Hyoid bone
04	1	Cricoid cartilage
	2	Thyroid cartilage of larynx
	3	Epiglottis
	4	Vestibular folds (false vocal cord)
	5	Vocal cords (true vocal cord)
	6	Palatine tonsil
	7	Lingual tonsil
05	1	Trachea
	2	Right primary bronchus

	3	Left primary bronchus (is longer and narrower and lies more transversely than the right primary bronchus)
	4	Left secondary (lobar) bronchus
	5	Left tertiary (segmental) bronchus, colored portions. Each tertiary (segmental) bronchus supplies a segment of lung tissue called bronchopulmonary segment
06	1	Thyroid cartilage of larynx
	2	Cricoid cartilage of larynx
	3	Trachea
	4	Thyroid gland
	5	Left primary bronchus
	6	Right primary bronchus
	7	Left secondary (lobar) bronchus
	8	Right secondary (lobar) bronchus
	9	Left tertiary bronchus
07	1	Thyroid cartilage of larynx
	2	Cricoid cartilage of larynx
	3	Trachea
	4	Thyrohyoid membrane
08	1	Cricoid cartilage of larynx
	2	Arytenoid cartilage of larynx
	3	Corniculate cartilage of larynx
	4	Cuneiform cartilage of larynx
	5	Epiglottis of larynx
09	1	Hyoid
	2	Thyrohyoid membrane
	3	Thyroid cartilage
	4	Cricoid cartilage
	5	Cartilages of trachea
10	1	Hyoid
	2	Epiglottis
	3	Cuneiform cartilage
	4	Corniculate cartilage
	5	Arytenoid cartilage
	6	Glottis (The medial opening between vocal folds or true vocal cords).
11	1	Epiglottis
	2	Thyroid cartilage

	3	Cricoid cartilage
	4	Cricoid cartilage
	5	Vestibular fold (false vocal cord)
	6	Vocal fold (true vocal cord)
	7	Corniculate cartilage
	8	Trachea
12	1	Hyoid
	2	Epiglottis
	3	Thyroid cartilage
	4	Cricoid cartilage
	5	Thyroid gland
	6	C-shaped hyaline rings of trachea (tracheal cartilages)
	7	Laryngeal prominence (Adam's apple)
13	1	Frontal sinus
	2	Sphenoidal sinus
	3	Vestibule
	4	Inferior concha
	5	Middle meatus
	6	Opening of auditory (Eustachian or pharyngotympanic) tube
	7	Uvula of soft palate
	8	Nasopharynx
	9	Oropharynx
	10	Laryngophaynx
	11	Tongue
	12	Trachea
	13	Esophagus
14	1	Epiglottis
	2	Arytenoid cartilage
	3	Corniculate cartilage
	4	Cricoid cartilage
	5	Thyroid gland
	6	Posterior view of thyroid cartilage
	7	Trachealis muscle on posterior surface of trachea
15	1	Visceral pleura
	2	Visceral pleura
16	1	Superior lobe
	2	Middle lobe

	3	Inferior lobe
	4	Horizontal fissure
	5	Oblique fissure on right lung
	6	Right lung
17	1	Superior lobe
	2	Middle lobe
	3	Inferior lobe
	4	Horizontal fissure
	5	Oblique fissure
	6	Hilus (the region through which bronchi, pulmonary blood vessels, lymphatic vessels, and nerves enter and exit)
18	1	Oblique fissure
	2	Superior lobe
	3	Inferior lobe
	4	Base
	5	Apex
	6	Left lung
19	1	Superior lobe
	2	Inferior lobe
	3	Oblique fissure
	4	Base
	5	Hilus
20	1	Epiglottis
	2	Cricoid cartilage
	3	Arytenoid cartilage
	4	Corniculate cartilage
	5	Cuneiform cartilage
	6	Cartilage rings of trachea
21	1	Cuneiform cartilage
	2	Epiglottis
	3	Corniculate cartilage
	4	Vocal fold (true vocal cord)
	5	Glottis (Rima glottidis , rim glottis)
22	1	Nasopharynx
	2	Oropharynx
	3	Laryngopharynx (hypopharynx)
23	1	Inferior lobe

	2	Middle lobe
	3	Superior lobe
	4	Superior lobe
	5	Inferior lobe
	6	Oblique fissure
	7	Horizontal fissure
	8	Oblique fissure
	9	Apex of lung
	10	Base of lung
	11	Left lung
	12	Right lung
24	1	Inspiration
25	1	Expiration
26	1	Atmospheric pressure
	2	Intrapulmonary (intra-alveolar pressure)
	3	2 (intrapulmonary pressure). Air always go from higher pressure to lower pressure area.
27	1	Respiratory bronchiole
	2	Tertiary bronchus
	3	Terminal bronchiole
	4	Visceral pleura/Pulmonary pleura
28	1	Bronchioles
	2	Alveoli
	3	Squamous epithelium portion of pleura
29	1	Alveoli
	2	Dense capillary layer of pleura
	3	collagenous fiber layer of pleura
	4	Elastic fiber layer of pleura
	5	Epithelium (simple squamous) portion of pleura
30	1	Exchange (pulmonary) capillaries
	2	Alveolar sac
31	1	Epiglottis
	2	Hyoid

	3	Thyroid membrane
	4	Thyroid cartilage of larynx
	5	Cricothyroid ligament
	6	Cricoid cartilage
	7	Criotracheal ligament
	8	Thyroid muscle
	9	Cricothyroid muscle
	10	Thyroid gland
	11	Trachea
	12	C-shaped tracheal cartilage
	13	Carina, located at 5th thoracic vertebrae
	14	Right primary bronchus
	15	Left primary bronchus
	16	Right secondary (lobar0 bronchus
	17	Left secondary (lobar) bronchus
	18	Left tertiary (segmental) bronchi
	19	Each lung has ten (10) tertiary bronchi, that supply a bronchopulmonary segment
32	1	Epiglottis
	2	Thyroid cartilage
	3	Cuneiform cartilage
	4	Corniculate cartilage
	5	Arytenoid cartilage
	6	Posterior cricoarytenoid muscle
	7	Thyroid gland
	8	Trachea
	9	Transverse smooth muscle (trachealis muscle) and elastic connective tissue. Remember, the supportive hyaline cartilage in the trachea only goes is C-shape and only goes 3/4 around the tubular trachea.

	10	Left secondary (lobar) bronchi
	11	Right secondary (lobar) bronchi
	12	Left primary bronchus
	13	Right primary bronchus
	14	Tertiary (segmental) bronchi
33	1	Tracheal cartilage of the trachea
	2	Carina cartilage located at 5th thoracic vertebrae
	3	Right primary bronchus
	4	Left primary bronchus
	5	Secondary bronchus on right side
	6	Secondary bronchus on left side
	7	Tertiary bronchus on right side
	8	Tertiary bronchus on left side
34	1	Epiglottis cartilage
	2	Vestibular fold (false vocal cord)
	3	Thyroid cartilage
	4	Cricoid cartilage
	5	Vocal fold (true vocal cord)
	6	Cricoid cartilage
	7	Trachea
	8	C-shaped tracheal cartilage
	9	Cuneiform cartilage
	10	Corniculate cartilage

35	1	Epiglottis
	2	Body of hyoid
	3	Thyrohyoid membrane
	4	Thyroid cartilage
	5	Laryngeal prominence (Adam's apple)
	6	Cricothyroid ligament
	7	Cricoid cartilage
	8	Cricotracheal ligament
	9	Right lobe of thyroid gland
	10	Cartilage of trachea
36	1	Parathyroid gland (located on posterior surface of thyroid gland lobe)
	2	Right lobe of thyroid gland
	3	Cricoid cartilage
	4	Arytenoid cartilage
	5	Corniculate cartilage
	6	Thyroid cartilage
	7	Epiglottis
	8	Cuneiform cartilage

RESPIRATORY SYSTEM
DISSECTIONS
ANSWERS

Picture #	Question #	answers
01	1	Left lung
	2	Trachea
	3	Left primary bronchus
	4	Right secondary bronchus
	5	Bronchus
02	1	Epiglottis
03	1	Thyroid cartilage of larynx
	2	Trachea of cat
04	1	Epiglottis of cat larynx

RESPIRATORY SYSTEM
HISTOLOGY
ANSWERS

Picture #	Question #	Answers
01	1	Cross section of trachea
02	1	Ciliated pseudostratified columnar epithelial tissue
03	1	Ciliated pseudostratified columnar epithelial tissue
04	1	Goblet cells producing mucus
05	1	Alveoli
	2	Bronchiole (note the wrinkled appearance of the lumen due to lack of cartilage)
06	1	Bronchiole
	2	Alveoli
07	1	Lung
	2	Alveoli
08	1	Lung
	2	Alveoli
09	1	Bronchus
	2	Cartilage (this gives support to bronchus)
10	1	Bronchiole (note the wrinkled inner surface since there is no cartilage to give support)

DIGESTIVE SYSTEM
MODELS
ANSWERS

Picture #	Question #	answers
01	1	Hard palate
	2	Uvula of soft palate
	3	Palatine tonsil
	4	Palatopharyngeal arch
	5	Palatoglossal arch
	6	Sublingual tonsil
	7	Tongue
	8	Lower lip (labia)
	9	Vestibule
02	1	Submandibular salivary gland
	2	Submandibular (Wharton's) duct
	3	Sublingual salivary gland
03	1	Parotid salivary gland
	2	Parotid (Stensen's) duct
04	1	Mesocolon
	2	Taeniae coli
	3	Haustra
05	1	Tongue
	2	Sublingual salivary gland
	3	Submandibular salivary gland
06	1	Circumvallate papilla
	2	Fungiform papillae
	3	Filiform papillae
	4	Lingual tonsil
07	1	Incisors
	2	Cuspid or canines
	3	Premolars or bicuspids
08	1	Crown
	2	Neck
	3	Root
	4	Enamel
	5	Dentin

09	1	Enamel
	2	Dentin
	3	Pulp
	4	Pulp cavity
10	1	Crown
	2	Root
	3	Neck
	4	Enamel of crown
	5	Dentin (forms basic shape of tooth and strength)
	6	Premolar (bicuspid)
	7	Incisor
11	1	Esophagus in thoracic cavity
	2	Esophagus pierces the diaphragm into abdominal cavity
12	1	Pancreas
	2	Accessory duct (duct of Santorini)
	3	Pancreatic duct (duct of Wirsung)
	4	Duodenum or duodenal portion of small intestine
	5	Adrenal gland
	6	Spleen
	7	Gall bladder
	8	Part of liver
13	1	Hepatopancreatic ampulla (ampulla of Vater)
	2	Sphincter of Oddi (major duodenal papilla)
	3	Pancreatic duct (duct of Wirsung)
	4	Common bile duct
14	1	Liver
	2	Gall bladder
	3	Left and right hepatic ducts
	4	Common hepatic duct
	5	Common bile duct
	6	Cystic duct
15	1	Mucosa
	2	Submucosa
	3	Muscularis externa
	4	Serosa
	5	Villus

	6	Lacteal (lymphatic capillary)
	7	Muscularis mucosae
	8	Simple columnar epithelium with goblet cells
16	1	Right lobe of liver
	2	Left lobe of liver
	3	Falciform ligament
	4	Taeniae coli
	5	Greater omentum
	6	Jejunum of the small intestine
	7	Stomach
	8	Esophagus
17	1	Cardia (cardiac region) of the stomach
	2	Fundus of the stomach
	3	Body of the stomach
	4	Pyloric portion of the stomach
	5	Lesser curvature
	6	Greater curvature
	7 "A:	Circular layer of smooth muscle
	8 "B"	Oblique layer of smooth muscle
	9 "C"	Longitudinal layer of smooth muscle
18	1	Esophagus
	2	Fundus of the stomach
	3	Body of the stomach
	4	Rugae of the stomach mucosa
	5	Pyloric (pylorus) of the stomach
	6	Pyloric sphincter (valve)
	7	Duodenum of the small intestine
19	1	Esophagus
	2	Cardia (cardiac region) of the stomach
	3	Fundus of the stomach
	4	Greater curvature
	5	Pyloric of the stomach
	6	Duodenum of the small intestine
	7	Pancreas
	8	Esophagus
20	1	Right lobe of liver

	2	Left lobe of liver
	3	Falciform ligament
21	1	Right lobe of liver
	2	Left lobe of liver
	3	Caudate lobe of liver a(near inferior vena cava)
	4	Quadrate lobe of liver (near gall bladder)
	5	Inferior vena cava
	6	Round ligament (ligamentum teres). The round ligament, which is the remnant of the umbilical vein, is located on the free inferior edge (border) of the falciform ligament extending to the umbilicus.
	7	Gall bladder
	8	Cystic duct
	9	Right and left hepatic ducts
	10	Common bile duct
22	1	Esophagus
	2	Cardia (cardiac region) of the stomach
	3	Fundus of the stomach
	4	Pyloric of the stomach
	5	Lesser omentum
	6	Greater omentum
	7	Longitudinal layer of smooth muscle
	8	Circular layer of smooth muscle
	9	Oblique layer of smooth muscle
23	1	Esophagus
	2	Cardia (cardiac region) of the stomach
	3	Fundus of the stomach
	4	Body of the stomach
	5	Pyloric of the stomach
	6	Pyloric sphincter
	7	Duodenum of the small intestine
	8	Rugae
24	1	Ileum of the small intestine
	2	Cecum
	3	Vermiform appendix
	4	Ileocecal (valve) sphincter
	5	Ascending colon
	6	Right colic (hepatic) flexure

	7	Transverse colon
	8	Left colic (splenic) flexure
	9	Descending colon
	10	Sigmoid colon
	11	Rectum
	12	Anal canal
25	1	Sigmoid colon
	2	Anus
	3	Internal anal sphincter (smooth muscle which is involuntary)
	4	External anal sphincter (skeletal muscle which is voluntary)
	5	Rectum (In the pelvis, at the level of the third sacral vertebra, the sigmoid colon joins the rectum, which runs posteroinferiorly just in front of the sacrum)
	6	rectum
26	1	Parotid salivary gland
	2	Parotid (Stensen's) duct
27	1	Left lobe of liver
	2	Right lobe of liver
	3	Stomach
	4	Teniae coli
	5	Haustra
	6	Jejunum portion of small intestine
	7	Greater omentum
28	1	Palatoglossal arch
	2	Palatopharyngeal arch
	3	Uvula of soft palate
	4	Oropharynx
29	1	Uvula of soft palate
	2	Palatine tonsil
	3	Oropharynx
	4	Tongue
30	1	Uvula of soft palate
	2	Palatoglossal arch
	3	Palatopharyngeal arch
	4	Palatine tonsil
	5	Hard palate forming roof of mouth
	6	Oropharynx

	7	Tongue
31	1	Inferior vena cava
	2	Falciform ligament
	3	Gall bladder
	4	Right lobe
	5	Left lobe
	6	Caudate lobe
	7	Quadrate lobe
	8	Cystic duct
	9	Common bile duct
	10	Hepatic artery
	11	Hepatic portal vein
32	1	Right lobe of liver
	2	Left lobe of liver
	3	Caudate lobe of liver
	4	Inferior vena cava
	5	Falciform ligament
33	1	Right lobe of liver
	2	Left lobe of liver
	3	Gall bladder (this organ is not really green in body)
	4	Falciform ligament

DIGESTIVE SYSTEM
IIISTOLOGY
ANSWERS

Picture #	Question #	answers
01	1	Keratinized stratified squamous epithelial tissue of tongue
	2	Taste buds
02	1	Tongue
	2	Taste buds
03	1	Villi of small intestine
	2	mucosa
	3	Submucosa
	4	Muscularis
	5	Smooth muscle
	6	Two layers (circular and longitudinal) smooth muscles

04	1	Duodenum of small intestine (note Brunner's glands)
	2	ileum of small intestine (note Peyer's patches)
	3	jejunum of small intestine
	4	Serosa
	5	Submucosa
	6	Peyer's patches located in submucosa of ileum
05	1	Esophagus
	2	Muscular folds
06	1	Liver
	2	Lobule
	3	Central vein of liver lobule
07	1	Small intestine (duodenum)
	2	Mucosa
	3	Intestinal gland (crypt of Lieberkühn)
	4	Submucosa
	5	Duodenal (Brunner's) glands
08	1	Liver
09	1	Small intestine
10	1	Small intestine
11	1	Taste bud

URINARY SYSTEM
MODELS
ANSWERS

Picture #	Question #	answers
01	1	Right kidney
	2	Adrenal gland
	3	Renal capsule
	4	Renal pelvis of ureter
	5	Ureter
	6	Urinary bladder
	7	Abdominal aorta
	8	Renal artery
	9	Inferior vena cava
02	1	Right ureter
	2	Renal pelvis of right ureter
	3	Major calyx
	4	Minor calyces
	5	Renal pyramid
03	1	Renal capsule
	2	Renal hilus (where the ureters leave the kidney. Blood vessels, lymphatic vessels and nerves enter and exit the kidney
04	1	Ureter
	2	Major calyces
	3	Minor calyces
	4	Renal papilla (papillae) or papilla pyramid
	5	Renal pyramid
05	1	Right kidney
	2	Right ureter
	3	Urinary bladder in pelvic cavity
	4	Renal pelvis
	5	Major calyces
	6	Left ureter
06	1	Renal artery
	2	Segmental arteries
	3	Interlobar arteries
	4	Arcuate arteries
	5	Interlobular arteries

	6	Afferent arteriole
07	1	Ureter
	2	Renal pelvis
	3	Major calyx
	4	Minor calyx
	5	Renal pyramids
	6	Renal capsule of kidney
	7	Renal column (inward extension of cortical tissue located between renal pyramids)
08	1	Trigone of urinary bladder
	2	Urethra (takes urine away from urinary bladder)
09	1	Ureter
	2	Renal pelvis
	3	Major calyx
	4	Minor calyces
	5	Renal papillae
	6	Renal column (cortical area between renal pyramids)
	7	Arcuate vein
	8	Interlobar artery
	9	Interlobular artery
10	1	Major calyx
	2	Minor calyx
	3	Renal papillae (apex end of renal pyramid)
	4	Cortex of kidney
	5	Collecting tubules (renal pyramids appear striped because of the collecting tubules and the loops of Henle)
11	1	Renal pelvis of ureter
	2	Major calyx
	3	Minor calyx
	4	Cortex
12	1	Proximal convoluted tubule (PCT) of nephron
	2	Parietal layer of glomerular (Bowman's) capsule
	3	Capsular space
	4	Glomerulus
	5	Afferent arteriole
	6	Efferent arteriole (diameter is smaller than afferent arteriole)
	7	Macula densa (a group of cells that are chemoreceptors or osmoreceptors that respond to changes in the solute content of the filtrate)

13	1	Visceral layer of Glomerular (Bowman's)capsule
	2	Podocytes
	3	Pedicles
14	1	Renal corpuscle
	2	Proximal convoluted tubule (PCT)
	3	Descending loop (limb) of Henle or thin limb of the loop of Henle
	4	Ascending loop (limb) of Henle or thick limb of the loop of Henle
	5	Distal convoluted tubule (DCT)
	6	Collecting duct
	7	Arcuate artery
	8	Interlobular artery
15	1	Cortical nephron
	2	Juxtamedullary nephron
16	1	Glomerular capillaries (glomerulus)
	2	Proximal convoluted tubule (PCT)
	3	Bowman's capsule
	4	Podocyte
	5	Interlobular artery
	6	Ascending or thick limb of the loop of Henle
	7	Renal corpuscle
17	1	Afferent arteriole
	2	Efferent arteriole
	3	Macula densa
	4	Glomerular capillaries (glomerulus)
	5	Capsular space in Bowman's capsule
	6	Parietal layer of glomerular (Bowman's) capsule
	7	Proximal convoluted tubule (PCT)
18	1	Renal corpuscle
	2	Proximal convoluted tubule
	3	Descending limb of Henle
	4	Ascending limb of Henle
	5	Distal convoluted tubule (DCT)
	6	Collecting duct
19	1	Cortex of kidney
	2	Renal pyramid
	3	Renal column
	4	Collecting ducts

	5	Renal papilla (apex of renal pyramids)
	6	Minor calyx
20	1	Ureteral openings into bladder
	2	Trigone
	3	Internal urethral orifice (opening to urethra)
	4	Detrusor muscle
	5	Prostate gland
	6	Urethra
	7	Internal urethral sphincter (involuntary sphincter keeps urethra closed when urine is not being passed and prevents leaking of urine)
21	1	Ductus deferens
	2	Seminal vesicle
	3	Prostate gland
22	1	Glomerular (Bowman's) capsule
	2	Glomerulus
	4	Afferent arteriole
	5	Efferent arteriole
	6	Proximal convoluted tubule
	7	Descending limb of the loop of Henle
	8	Ascending limb of the loop of Henle
	9	Distal convoluted tubule
	10	Collecting duct
	11	Distal convoluted tubule
	12	Peritubular capillary network located in cortex region of kidney
	13	Interlobular artery
	14	Arcuate artery
	15	Arcuate vein
	16	Interlobular vein
	17	Interlobar vein
	26	Vasa recta

URINARY SYSTEM
DISSECTIONS
ANSWERS

Picture #	Question #	answers
01	1	Cortex
	2	Renal pyramid in medulla of kidney

	3	Minor calyx
	4	Major calyx
02	1	Renal capsule
	2	Cortex
	3	Renal pyramid in medulla of kidney
	4	Major calyx
	5	Minor calyx
	6	Hilus (renal hilus) of kidney
	7	Ureter

URINARY SYSTEM
HISTOLOG
ANSWERS

Picture #	Question #	answers
01	1	Kidney
	2	Renal corpuscle
02	1	Capsular space of Bowman's capsule
	2	Glomerulus
03	1	Kidney
	2	Glomerulus
04	1	Proximal convoluted tubule (PCT)
	2	Glomerulus
	3	Capsular space of Bowman's capsule
05	1	Kidney
	2	Renal corpuscle

THE REPRODUCTIVE SYSTEM (MALE)
MODELS
ANSWERS

Picture #	Question #	answers
01	1	Glans penis
	2	Scrotum
	3	Testis
	4	Epididymis
	5	Spermatic cord (composed of ductus deferens, blood vessels, nerves and lymphatic vessels)
	6	Urinary bladder

	7	Ductus (vas) deferens
	8.	Ureter
	9	Rectum (colon)
	10	Seminal vesicle
	11	Prostate gland
02	1	Urinary bladder
	2	Ureter leading into urinary bladder
	3	Prostate gland
	4	Ejaculatory duct
	5	Seminal vesicle
03	1	Urinary bladder
	2	Seminal vesicles
	3	Prostate gland
	4	Crus of penis
	5	Bulbourethral (Cowper's) glands
04	1	Testis
	2	Epididymis
	3	Spermatic cord
	4	Seminal vesicle
	5	Prostate gland
05	1	Glans penis (composed of corpus spongiosum)
	2	Penile urethra
	3	Corpus cavernosum
	4	Corpus cavernosum
	5	Prostatic urethra
	6	Ejaculatory duct
	7	Seminal vesicle
	8	Corpus spongiosum
06	1	Urogenital diaphragm
	2	Bulbourethral (Cowper's) gland
	3	Prostatic urethra
	4	Membranous urethra
	5	Penile urethra
	6	Ejaculatory duct
07	1	Corpus cavernosum
	2	Penile urethra

	3	Corpus spongiosum
	4	Testis
	5	Epididymis
	6	Urinary bladder
	7	Rectum (colon)
	8	Ureter
08	1	Corpus cavernosum
	2	Corpus spongiosum
	3	Urethra within corpus spongiosum within penis
09	1	Urinary bladder
	2	Ductus (Vas) deferens
	3	Seminal vesicle
	4	Prostate gland
10	1	Inguinal canal
	2	Cremaster muscle
	3	Dartos muscle
	4	Tunica vaginalis
	5	Tunica albuginea
11	1	Glans penis
	2	Shaft (body) of penis
	3	Crus of penis
	4	Bulbourethral (Cowper's) gland
	5	Prostate gland
	6	Seminal vesicle
	7	Urinary bladder
	8	Vas deferens
	9	Testis

THE REPRODUCTIVE SYSTEM (MALE)
DISSECTIONS
ANSWERS

Picture #	Question #	answers
01	1	Testis
	2	Ductus (vas) deferens
02	1	Tunica albuginea of testis
	2	Tail of epididymis

	3	Tunica vaginalis that surrounds tunica albunginea and testis
	4	Ductus (vas) deferens
03	1	Testis
	2	Body of epididymis
	3	Ductus (vas) deferens
	4	Tunica vaginalis
	5	Tail of epididymis
	6	Head of epididymis

THE REPRODUCTIVE SYSTEM (MALE)
HISTOLOGY
ANSWERS

Picture #	Question #	answers
01	1	Penis
	2	Corpora (corpus) cavernosa of penis
	3	Corpus spongiosum of penis
	4	Urethra (penile urethra)
02	1	Testis
	2	Epididymis
	3.	Spermatic cord
	4.	Gubernaculum
03	1	Head of sperm
	2	The head contains the nuclear material (DNA) and a lysosome-like structure called an acrosome, which contains enzymes (hyaluronidase and proteinases) that aid penetration of the sperm cell into a secondary oocyte. The nuclear material consists of 23 chromosomes in humans, 22 autosomes and one sex chromosome.
	3	Tail
04	1	Interstitial (Leydig) cells
	2	Produce male sex hormones (androgens)
05	1	Testis
06	1	Sperm (spermatozoa or spermatozoon)
07	1	Seminiferous tubules
	2	Site of spermatogenesis (sperm production)
	3	Interstitial (Leydig) cells

THE REPRODUCTIVE SYSTEM (FEMALE)
MODELS

Picture #	Question #	answers
01	1	Mons pubis
	2	Labium majora (majus)
	3	Labium minor (minus)
	4	Urinary bladder
	5	Left ureter
	6	Uterus
	7	Round ligament
	8	Uterine (fallopian) tube
	9	Infundibulum with fimbriae
	10	Vagina
	11	Left uterine (fallopian) tube
02	1	Ovary
	2	Ovarian ligament
	3	Uterine (fallopian) tube
	4	Round ligament
	5	Fimbriae
	6	Vagina
	7	Labia minora
	8	Labia majora
03	1	Mons pubis
	2	Symphysis pubis of pelvic girdle
	3	Clitoris
	4	Labia majora (labium majus)
	5	Labia minora (labium minus)
	6	Urinary bladder
	7	Urethra
	8	Fundus of uterus
	9	Body of uterus
	10	Cervix of uterus
	11	Vagina
04	1	Clitoris
	2	Labia minora (labium minus)
	3	vestibule
	4	Vaginal orifice
	5	Anus

05	1	Round ligament
	2	Uterine (fallopian) tube
	3	Ovary
	4	Fimbriae of uterine tube
	5	Infundibulum
	6	Fundus of uterus
	7	Labia majora (labium majus)
06	1	Fundus of uterus
	2	Body of uterus
	3	Cervix of uterus
	4	Round ligament
	5	Clitoris
	6	Rectum
07	1	Fornix of vagina
	2	Vesicouterine pouch
	3	Urethra
	4	Uterine cavity
	5	Cervical canal
	6	Ovary
	7	Rectouterine pouch
08	1	Fundus of uterus
	2	Urinary bladder
	3	Uterine (Fallopian) tube
	4	Mons pubis of vulva
09	1	Mesosalpinx
	2	Mesovarian
	3	Mesometrium
10	1	Cervix of uterus
	2	Mesovarium located between the two folds of the broad ligament suspends the ovary.
	3	Broad ligament
11	1	Fundus of uterus
	2	Uterine cavity
	3	Cervical cavity
	4	Ovarian ligament
	5	Broad ligament
	6	Isthmus of uterine tube

	7	Infundibulum of uterine tube
	8	Rugae of vagina
	9	Internal os
12	1	Perimetrium
	2	Myometrium
	3	Endometrium
13	1	Broad ligament
	2	Myometrium
	3	Stratum functionalis of the endometrium. The layer closer to the uterine cavity. This layer undergoes cyclic changes in response to ovarian hormones and is discharged during menstruation.
	4	Fornix of vagina
14	1	Suspensory ligament
	2	Mesovarium ligament
	3	Mesosalpinx ligament
	4	Ovarian ligament
15	1	Pubic symphysis
	2	Uterine tube (Oviduct)
	3	Round Ligament
	4	Fundus of Uterus
	5	Labia majora (majorus)
	6	Labia minora (minus)
16	1	Fundus of uterus
	2	Uterine tube (Oviduct)
	3	Rectum
	4	Fimbria
	5	Ureter
17	1	Labia majora (majorus)
	2	Labia minora (minus)
	3	Ureter
	4	Bartholin's gland (Greater vestibular gland)
	5	External anal sphincter
	6	Anus
18	1	Round ligament
	2	Uterine tube (Oviduct)
	3	Ovarian ligament
	4	Ovary
	5	Uterosacral ligament

	6	Broad ligament
	7	Fundus
	8	Body
19	1	Fat
	2	Lymphatic vessels
	3	Nipple
	4	Areola
	5	Lactiferous duct
	6	Lactiferous gland
20	1	Uterine tube (Oviduct)
	2	Infundibulum
	3	Fimbria
	4	Rugae of vaginal canal
	5	Cervix
	6	Ovary
	7	Round ligament
	8	Fundus

THE REPRODUCTIVE SYSTEM (FEMALE)
HISTOLOGY
ANSWERS

Picture #	Question #	answers
01	1	Ovary
	2	Primordial follicle
	3	Primary follicle
	4.	Graafian (mature) follicle
	5	Zona pellucida
	6	Secondary oocyte
02	1	Primordial follicle
03	1	Graafian (mature) follicle
	2	Antrum filled with follicular fluid
	3	Secondary oocyte
	4	Zona pellucida
	5	Corona radiata of granulosa cells (innermost layer of granulosa cell becomes firmly attached to the zona pellucida)
04	1	Primordial follicles within ovary
05	1	Graafian (mature) follicle
06	1	Ovary
07	1	Corpus luteum

08	1	Corpus luteum
09	1	Primordial follicles
	2	Secondary (antral) follicle
10	1	Corpus luteum
11	1	Corpus albicans in ovary